BROUDE BROTHERS LIMITED
MUSIC
56 WEST 45 STREET
NEW YORK, N. Y. 10036

SOLE SELLING AGENT
ALEXANDER BROUDE, INC.
120 W. 57th STREET — NEW YORK, N.Y. 10019

The Treasury of

ENGLISH
CHURCH
MUSIC

General Editors: GERALD H. KNIGHT and WILLIAM L. REED

The Treasury of ENGLISH

BLANDFORD PRESS : LONDON

CHURCH MUSIC

Volume ONE 1100 – 1545

Edited by DENIS STEVENS

Foreword by FRANK Ll. HARRISON

652933

FIRST PUBLISHED IN 1965
© BLANDFORD PRESS LIMITED
167 HIGH HOLBORN, LONDON, W.C.1

LIBRARY OF CONGRESS
CATALOGUE NUMBER 65-25006

MUSIC LAYOUT BY R. T. MATTHEWS AND ENGRAVED BY
LOWE & BRYDONE (PRINTERS) LTD., VICTORIA ROAD, LONDON, N.W.10
FILMSET IN BASKERVILLE BY BOOKPRINT LIMITED, CRAWLEY, SUSSEX.
PRINTED IN GREAT BRITAIN BY LOWE & BRYDONE (PRINTERS) LTD. AND
BOUND BY RICHARD CLAY (THE CHAUCER PRESS) LTD., BUNGAY, SUFFOLK.

GENERAL EDITORS' PREFACE

IT is perhaps not unreasonable to state that no other country possesses so fine and unbroken a choral tradition as England, and to claim that English Church music at its best compares with the finest to be found anywhere in the world.

Like the householder in the Gospel, the editors have sought to bring forth out of this 'treasure, things new and old', from the earliest experiments in polyphony to the challenging compositions of today, and in the compilation of the first three volumes they have been assisted by eminent musicians, each of whom is a specialist in his own field.

Volume 1, which covers the earliest period to the Reformation, is edited by Denis Stevens.

Volume 2, representing the 'golden age' from the Reformation until the death of Charles I, is edited by Peter le Huray.

Volume 3, containing works from the early days of the Commonwealth to the accession of George III, is edited by Christopher Dearnley.

Much of the material in the above volumes is published for the first time, and a number of well-known pieces appear in newly-edited versions.

Volume 4 covers the period from 1760 to 1900, and includes an introduction by George Guest.

Volume 5 contains the works of twentieth-century composers (British, Canadian, Australian, and American) and includes an introduction by David Lumsden.

It is hoped that this publication will stimulate all who have an interest in Church Music to explore further the treasures that exist. What is of even greater importance, it is hoped that choirs throughout the world will be encouraged to sing this music worthily to the glory of God, for their own inspiration and that of very many others who listen to it.

GERALD H. KNIGHT
WILLIAM L. REED

Alleluia—Per te Dei genetrix

(Oxford, Bodleian Library, Lat. liturg. d. 20, fol. 15v.)

CONTENTS

THE MUSIC

ACKNOWLEDGMENTS

ACKNOWLEDGMENT is due to those publishers who have given permission for the inclusion of copyright material as indicated at the foot of the music pages, and as listed below:

Alleluia post partem	© 1958	Frank Ll. Harrison
Fulget caelestis curia	© 1944	University of California Press
Ave miles caelestis	© 1951	Manfred Bukofzer
Angelus ad virginem	© 1963	Novello & Co. Ltd.
Deo gracias persolvamus	© 1958	Royal Musical Association
Veni sancte spiritus	© 1953	Hinrichsen Edition Ltd.
Regina caeli laetare	© 1953	Royal Musical Association and American Musicological Society
Quam pulchra es	© 1953	Royal Musical Association and American Musicological Society
Gloria, laus et honor	© 1963	Oxford University Press
Salve virgo mater	© 1959	Armen Carapetyan, Director of the American Institute of Musicology
Ave Maria mater Dei	© 1961	Royal Musical Association
Magnificat ('Regale')	© 1961	Royal Musical Association
Magnificat	© 1963	Edmund Harding
Agnus Dei	© 1962	Stainer & Bell Ltd.

D.W.S.

Ave miles caelestis curiae
(Oxford, Bodleian Library, E mus. 7, page x)

FOREWORD

by FRANK Ll. HARRISON
Reader in the History of Music in the University of Oxford

THE publication of a volume such as this is a welcome manifestation of the place music is beginning to have in current views of British history. Though a good deal of medieval music from continental sources has been published in this century and there are several general anthologies (not originating here), much English medieval music is still unpublished. This volume is the first to present in complete samples a review of sacred part-music in England and Scotland from the Conquest to the Reformation. As such it takes its place beside long-accepted works on medieval British literature, drama, architecture, sculpture and painting.

It has often been said that the particular Englishness of English music is the result of its being incorrigibly conservative. If English medieval music had simply dogged French music several steps behind, its interest for musicians today would indeed be merely historical and parochial. Its case is not so simple, nor yet is it one of musical practices persisting so long that they came to be regarded as characteristic rather than just old-fashioned—a fairly familiar phenomenon at any time. The story of English medieval music is broadly that of originally common and universal techniques being developed over a long period and reapplied in a variety of new contexts to such a degree that the effect on contemporary hearers was often that of a fresh and original creation. For example, the technique of melodic exchange called *rondellus*, which was everywhere in the twelfth century, judging from surviving examples, came during the following two centuries to be regarded as something typically English (see Nos. 3, 12, 13 and 15 in this volume). Specimens were copied into at least one French motet collection in the late thirteenth century. Pieces like these inevitably have a fascination because of their ingenious and imaginative crossing of different strains of musical practice.

Paradoxically, the same tenacity of musical habits was partly responsible for English music in the fifteenth century being as fashionable and as widely copied as any in Europe, so that Johannes Tinctoris, musician of Ferdinand I of Naples, could say that the new music of his day had had its fount and origin among the English, with

Dunstable as their star figure. It is true to say that the complex interaction between English and French music which took place about the time of the Council of Constance and the battle of Agincourt led to new notions of part-writing and new concepts of musical beauty, most of which have continued to be operative in Western music. The composers Olyver, Thomas Damett and Leonel Power, all three represented here, were prominent among those who infused the unadorned English traditional 'descant' with the artifices of the French courtly *chanson* at the turn of the century, contemporary with the poetry of Christine de Pisan and the miniatures of the *atelier* of Boucicault. A few decades later John Dunstable's serenely mature version of this synthesis, shown perhaps at its best in his widely-known *Veni Sancte Spiritus* (possibly written for Henry VI's coronation in Paris in 1431) was being taken as the epitome of modern taste by Philip of Burgundy's composers Guillaume Dufay and Gilles Binchois. Martin le Franc's famous passage in *Le Champion des Dames* on the state of music in France, in which he observed that Dufay and Binchois

> . . . ont pris de la contenance
> Angloise et ensuy Dunstable

is too true to the evidence of their music to be dismissed as an amateur's misconception.

The qualities in music which make it eloquent and meaningful across centuries of history or chasms of cultural and religious difference are self-evident and self-authenticating, but rarely explicable. No amount of technical explanation can take the place of this living contact, or without it bridge completely the differences in daily horizons of thought and lifelong social and religious rituals which separate us from British musicians of the Middle Ages. But the music in this volume is all historically informative and illuminating, and much of it may communicate its own unique quality of meaning across the divisions of time, sense and musical purpose.

Frank Ll. Harrison

Jesus College, Oxford.
April, 1965.

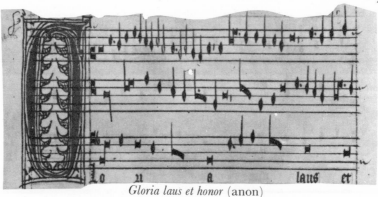

Gloria laus et honor (anon)
(British Museum, Egerton MS. 3307, fol. 10v.)

INTRODUCTION

WRITING towards the end of that half-millennium whose musical culture forms the basis and background of the present volume, a Scottish theologian and historiographer, admirably lacking in chauvinism, gave his considered reasons for the excellence of English music and musicians:

> In England every village, be it only of twelve or thirteen houses, has a parish church; their places of worship are most richly adorned, and in the art of music they stand, in my opinion, first in all Europe. For though in France or in Scotland you may meet with some musicians of such absolute accomplishment as in England, yet 'tis not in such numbers.

John Major's *Historia Majoris Britanniae tam Angliae quam Scotiae* was published in Paris in 1521, but the thoughts expressed in those two sentences about music might equally well apply to the previous centuries of Plantagenet rule, when English music as we know it first developed as a truly national, even international art. Besides the villages and parish churches, there were collegiate churches, royal establishments, and cathedrals of many kinds; and there were monasteries, friaries, and nunneries in such profusion that a simple index of them would run to many hundreds of entries. Many of these institutions adorned their services with polyphony ranging from simple extemporization to relatively complex written music, and this extensive gamut of types and techniques has been freely drawn upon for the selection offered in the following pages.

The principal end and aim of this edition is a practical one. For those in search of musicological texts, often unsuitable for performance, there exists an ample supply of monumental secondary sources furnished for the most part with detailed collation of original manuscripts and learned accounts of notational palaeography. In sparing the amateur choral conductor from such scholarly delights as these, I have no wish to deter him from further study, should he choose not to accept my readings. In each and every case I list the original source or sources, and any facsimiles that may be easily available. I sincerely hope that he will have recourse to them if doubt should at any time enter his mind, for only by personally investigating primary source-material can we gain the fullest insight into character and idiom, whether of music or of anything written down and preserved throughout the ages.

Since the compositions I have chosen range from the eleventh to the sixteenth centuries, it seemed to me unwise to make a fetish of standardization and consistency in view of the enormously wide variations in style, content, and scope of this repertoire.

Although I am in favour of maintaining a fixed ratio of note-reduction when dealing with the work of one composer or the output of one century, I realize that the time-span of the present volumes precludes any such neat and tidy solution. I have even found room for a deliberate experiment, juxtaposing two different reduction scales for the two items by Taverner, in the hope that some readers and conductors will write and tell me which they prefer. Recent years and recent editions have seen a move in the direction of quartering, rather than halving of note-values, and I have heard singers murmur that this is going too far. Fashions in transcription tend to change fairly rapidly, if the past half-century is anything to go by, and I feel that the future may see a return to halving the note-values by popular demand.

Having at various times suffered the frustrating experience of trying to use a book whose information has been so separated and parcelled out that hour upon hour must be spent in order to understand it and relate the parts to the whole, I have decided (with the kindly consent of the General Editors of this series) to re-unite all the information necessary for the appreciation and performance of this music in the following Commentary. This may be used as a basis for programme notes, provided that due and proper acknowledgement is made, as well as for further reading and listening.

It is my pleasant duty to thank those of my friends and colleagues who have agreed to the reproduction of their editions, and for so generously allowing me to make occasional and minor changes in the interests of practical performance. For deep insight into this matter, I wish to thank my Ambrosian Singers, who for well over a decade have worked with me in concerts, broadcasts, and recordings in order to share with music-lovers all over the world our own enthusiasm for medieval and Renaissance polyphony of liturgical origin. To Dr. Gerald Knight and Dr. W. L. Reed, as to Mr. Terence Goldsmith of the Blandford Press, I offer my sincere gratitude for their apparently inexhaustible patience with an uncommonly evasive editor; especially to Dr. Reed, who shouldered the burden of making pianoforte reductions, and helped me immeasurably at the proof-reading stage. Whatever defects remain should by rights be blamed on to me; and if I can say *mea culpa* instead of *mea maxima culpa* I shall feel that my labours have not been in vain.

DENIS STEVENS
Columbia University in the City of New York
February, 1965.

COMMENTARY ON THE MUSIC

1. anon., **Sancte Dei pretiose** (Oxford, Bodleian Library, MS. Bodley 572, f.49v).
Facsimile: *Early English Harmony* (1897) pl. 1; *Early Bodleian Music* (1913) pl. xvi;
Apel: *Notation of Polyphonic Music*, p. 205.
The MS. gives no indication of rhythm or metre, and letter-notation is used to denote
pitch. Written down with other liturgical texts at the end of a school book, probably
from St. Augustine's, Canterbury, this two-part Verse *Ut tuo propitiatus* has been generally hailed as the first known example of English polyphony. The Customary of
St. Augustine's permitted simple harmonization of Sequence, *Benedictus*, and *Magnificat*
on principal feasts, and this may have been extended to include the verse of a responsory. Not infrequently the form of a responsory traced a complex pattern, both as
regards music and text, and a complete transcription would run to a length far beyond
the scope of this publication. This is true in the case of *Sancte Dei pretiose*, sung on the
eve of St. Stephen's Day at the procession to the altar of that saint, and again as the
ninth responsory at Matins on the same day. The Sarum Breviary shows, as do most of
the plainsong sources, that the responsory *in toto* contained a prose:

> R. Sancte Dei pretiose
>   protomartyr Stephane,
>   qui virtute caritatis
>   circumfultus undique:
>
>   Dominum pro inimico
>   exorasti populo.
>   Funde preces pro devoto
>   tibi nunc collegio.
>
> V. Ut tuo propitiatus
>   interventu Dominus
>   nos purgatos a peccatis
>   iungat caeli civibus.
>
> R. Funde preces pro devoto
>   tibi nunc collegio.
>
> Prosa: Te mundi climata . . .
>
> R. Funde preces pro devoto
>   tibi nunc collegio.
>
> V. Gloria Patri et Filio
>   et Spiritui Sancto.
>
> R. Funde preces pro devoto
>   tibi nunc collegio.

Had the manuscript provided a harmonized setting of the prose *Te mundi climata*, it would have been well worth while to reproduce the entire composition, underlaying *Gloria Patri* to the music of *Ut tuo propitiatus* in the traditional manner. In the circumstances, however, the first section only has been given, using the plainsong of the *Sarum Antiphoner* (facsimile edition, 1901–26).

The Verse should be sung by soloists, nicely balanced as to weight of tone, even though the lower line represents the plainsong. The rhythmical setting is entirely my own, and I offer it with due reservations: it can be sung with as much freedom as may be desirable, though a steady tempo is recommended in order that the text can be clearly audible, especially in a resonant building.

2. anon., **Alleluia: Post partum** (Wolfenbüttel, Ducal Library, MS. 677, f.181). Facsimile: *An Old St. Andrews Music Book* (1931).

One of the principal sources of thirteenth-century polyphony in Britain is a volume compiled for the Augustinian Priory of St. Andrews, and consisting largely of French music. Internal and liturgical evidence suggests that local composers nevertheless took a hand in certain additions to the main corpus, especially in a collection of polyphonic music for Masses of the B.V.M. The frequent cadences on either fifths or unisons or octaves will sound more satisfactorily in tune if vibrato is reduced at these points. Indeed, great finesse of intonation is of vital importance in exposed two-part texture of this nature. Note that the melodic flourish following the word *'genitrix'* in the lower voice has been set out in a regularly recurring pattern of three notes and a rest, foreshadowing the careful rhythmic organization of later clausulae and motets.

3. anon., **Perspice Christicola** (London, British Museum, MS. Harley 978, f.11v). Facsimile: *Grove's Dictionary of Music* (5th edition) Vol. VII, frontispiece.

This composition is best known in its secular guise as *Sumer is icumen in*, and has survived recent debates about the date of its origin, besides yielding new information concerning its form and content. Frank Ll. Harrison, in his *Music in Medieval Britain* (1958) has pointed out that the composer devised twelve separate melodies over a two-part ground, which in medieval times went by the name of *rondellus*. Since the upper parts form a self-contained round, or *rota*, capable of being sung by two, three, or four voices, the harmonic content is adequately rich to begin with; and when the two-part ground is added below, a texture ranging from four to six parts emerges with apparently spontaneous charm and effortless poise. But the structure is more subtle than at first appears, for in spite of the two-bar ground, the twelve separate melodies join together to form one continuous whole, proceeding not in two-bar phrases but in a complex of 4+4+2+4+4+6 bars. The Latin poem calls upon the followers of Christ to join in celebrating the Resurrection, and although the ground has no words, its melody coincides with the first five notes of *Regina caeli laetare*, the Marian antiphon sung during the Easter season. In revealing this hitherto unnoticed fact, Harrison suggests that a correct description of the piece would be 'rota-rondellus-motet: *Perspice Christicola*—Pes duplex *Regina caeli*'. If this seems too speculative, singers of the ground can always use some non-committal solmization syllable.

4. anon., **Miles Christi gloriose** (London, Westminster Abbey, MS. 33327, f.2v).
Facsimile: Dittmer, *Publications of Medieval Musical MSS.*, No. 5, p. 74.
The existence of this double-leaf, all that remains of a finely written volume of liturgical
polyphony compiled in the early thirteenth century, was first pointed out by Manfred
Bukofzer in 1954. Although I photographed the leaves for him, with the kind permission of the Librarian of Westminster Abbey, Bukofzer was unable to work on them
before his death in 1955. The plainsong in the lowest voice of the four-part motet
appears in the original manuscript with only one small clue, the word *'ablue'*, which
Jeremy Noble identified·as the final word of the responsory *Miles Christi gloriose*.
Medieval composers frequently chose the end of a text, rather than the beginning, for
their musical elaborations since a final flourish (*melisma*) was common at this point in
the plainsong. The *melisma* would then be disposed in an appropriate pattern, in this
case similar to that of the word *'genitrix'* in *Alleluia: Post partum* (No. 2). The flowering of
plainsong into polyphony may also be considered as a climactic device, and for this
reason the change from the one into the other should be made as smoothly as possible.
For reasons of space (as in No. 1) the first section of the responsory only has been given.
Its full form would be as follows:

> R. Miles Christi gloriose
> Edwarde sanctissime,
> tuo pio interventu
> culpas nostras ablue.
>
> V. Ut caelestis regni sedem
> valeamus scandere.
>
> R. tuo pio interventu
> culpas nostras ablue.
>
> V. Gloria Patri et Filio
> et Spiritui Sancto.
>
> R. culpas nostras ablue.

In all probability, the medieval choirmaster would have chosen the third and last
appearance of the word *'ablue'* as the cue for the motet to begin. Although *Miles Christi
gloriose* can apply to any confessor, the second of the two tropes, or insertions (*Ave miles
O Edwarde*) makes it perfectly clear that this is a composition in honour of Edward the
Confessor. Accordingly his name has been added to the text of the chant at the required
point. Its place in the liturgy would be in the night office, as the ninth responsory of
Matins.

5. anon., **Epiphaniam Domino canamus** (Montpellier, Bibl. de l'Ecole de Médecine
MS. H 196 f.392; Oxford, New College MS. 362, f.86). Facsimile: Rokseth, *Polyphonies
du XIIIe siècle*, i, 392v; this being a photograph of the Montpellier version, which is
complete. The fragment in the New College guard-book consists of the duplum part
only.
Stylistic and liturgical features show that the pair of motets *Balaam inquit vaticinans;
Huic ut placuit* were almost certainly written by an English composer, yet there is

precious little (at first sight) by way of indication of their function within the liturgy. The lowest of the three parts has no text apart from very short verbal cues, but these were identified by Rokseth as verses from the Epiphany sequence *Epiphaniam Domino canamus*. Although the Sarum rite prescribed the *Balaam* melody for the singing of the Benedicamus with Alleluia at Vespers and Matins of Epiphany, the added text (or trope) does not bring in the words '*Benedicamus Domino*' as do so many of the Benedicamus substitutes (see the final page of No. 15, *Ave miles caelestis curiae*). It may therefore be surmised, in view of other known connections between sequences and motets, that these two verses were sung with their polyphonic superstructure at the appropriate point in the sequence itself. It is significant that the Sarum Missal in the Bibliothèque de l'Arsénal, Paris, gives the opening of *Epiphaniam* in the plainsong notation of the time; but when the verse *Balaam* is reached, the notation becomes measured instead of free, so that the singers can fit their words and melody to the metre of the two descanting voices. Accordingly the sequence melody, in the lowest part, has here been provided with the text of the sequence.

The result of this reveals the purpose as well as the structure of these paired compositions, for it was customary for each internal melodic section of a sequence to be sung four times. First, the section was sung to a text which may be designated as B, it was then repeated as a wordless melisma, usually on the vowel a. Still using the same melody, the singers would follow with the next line of text (B'), a twin to B; and finally would come the melisma once more on the vowel a. This arrangement can be clearly seen in *Epiphaniam*.

First the choir sings the verse *Balaam*, the words being clearly audible below the decorative counterpoint supplied by two soloists. Then, as the choir repeats the melody to a, the soloists (turn by turn) come into their own, singing a trope, that is an elaboration or commentary on what has gone before: *Balaam inquit vaticinans*. Their tunes and texts work out neatly on an exchange basis because of an internal melodic repeat in the sequence melody, except of course for the last four bars, which fulfil a cadential role. The same pattern is repeated when the semichorus sings *Et confringet*, still to the same melody. This time however there is no trope, for when the semichorus reverts to its melisma on a, the soloists make use of the same vowel, breaking up their counterpoints in a style known as hocket. Certain medieval princes of the church objected to hocketing, perhaps because it was badly performed, or because it was beyond their comprehension. Hocketing need not be performed jerkily or unpleasantly. In any case, a resonant building tends to cover the gaps, though they are perceptible enough to allow the plainsong to emerge with greater clarity than it would, for instance, in a motet with continuous vocal lines.

In *Huic ut placuit* the distribution of text and melisma is slightly and subtly different from what has gone before. The sequence text and the trope upon it are heard simultaneously at the outset, but when the semichorus makes its first repeat of the melody, the trope text (now in the other tenor part) can be heard without encumbrance. When the next verse appears (*Thure Deum praedicant*) the upper parts are so busy hocketing and weaving elaborate exchange patterns that further text embellishment is out of the question. In this way both the main text and its subsidiary tropes are given alternate prominence, yet continuously seem bound together by the fourfold repeated melody. After this delectable jubilation, the sequence goes its way in the accepted manner.

6. anon., **Salve sancta parens** (Worcester, Cathedral Library, MS. Add. 68, fragment xxxv *e*). Facsimile: Dom Anselm Hughes, *Worcester Mediæval Harmony* (1928), frontispiece.

The Introit sung at Masses of the B.V.M. from Purification to Advent was *Salve sancta parens*, and this four-part polyphonic setting presents the complete plainsong (except for the intonation '*Salve*') as underpinning to an exceptionally smooth and beautiful vocal superstructure. The solo lines move almost entirely in stepwise or broken-third progressions, and they are so arranged that one voice pauses while the other two sing. The eleven-bar phrases, of which there are six in all, consist always of 8 bars of music and 3 of rests, but this pattern is staggered among the soloists in such a manner as to create an impression of asymetric symmetry, a four-part chord occurring only at the first and eighth bar of each phrase. The unbroken succession of equal notes in the lowest voice also accounts for part of the general impression of serenity.

Each of the upper voices has a trope of the liturgical text, and all begin with the word '*Salve*' and end with the syllables '-*lorum*'. They have not so far been discovered in any other source, and may well have been written especially for the musical setting. This comprises the antiphon proper, and in adhering to the Sarum form (antiphon, psalm-verse, antiphon, *Gloria Patri*, antiphon) the polyphonic setting has been reserved for the second and third repetitions.

7. anon., **Alleluia: Per te Dei Genetrix** (Oxford, Bodleian Library, Lat.liturg.d.20, f.15v/16).

This troped Alleluia forms part of a Mass of the Nativity of the B.V.M., and makes use of the plainsong and text belonging to this feast. In its usual form, the Alleluia calls for an intonation ('*Alleluia*') by soloists, followed immediately by a repeat of this by the choir, who continue the chant in a long and expressive melody (*jubilus*) to the vowel *a*. Then comes the verse, sung by soloists, from whom the choir takes over to sing the last word, in this case '*salvatorem*'. The Alleluia section is then repeated. In its polyphonic form, the alternation of soloists and choir follows the same pattern, except that the soloists deal exclusively with the tropes. If so desired, the lowest line of the polyphony can be sung by a single voice, but in practice it may be found easier for a small chorus to sustain these notes. This they should do quietly, in order not to interfere with the more rapid declamation of the soloists in the verse especially.

8. anon., **Candens lilium columbina** (Oxford, Bodleian Library, Lat.liturg.d.20, f.28v; Cambridge, Pembroke College, MS. 228, f.IIv).

This motet in honour of the B.V.M. is cast in an apparently epigrammatic form made up entirely of four-bar phrases, but the individual vocal and instrumental lines are so contrived and set out that the ear of the listener perceives only an onward flow of subtly interchanging melodies. A closer view reveals considerable cunning in the economic use of materials, which may be expressed by the following diagram (each letter referring to a four-bar phrase):

$$I \qquad II \qquad I \qquad II \qquad I$$
$$A\,B\,A\,C\,/\,D\,E\,B\,D\,E\,C\,/\,A\,B\,A\,C\,/\,D'\,E\,B\,D'\,E\,C\,/\,A\,B\,A\,C$$
$$16 \qquad 24 \qquad 16 \qquad 24 \qquad 16$$

Note that phrases B and C occur in both sections I and II, whereas of the other phrases A is found only in section I, and DE (or D'E) only in section II.

Although the two instrumental lines may be safely entrusted to the organ, they could also be played by two violas, cellos, bassoons, or any combination of these. The organ was of course the principal purveyor of instrumental solos and accompaniments in the medieval church, but there are occasional references to the use of shawms, or reed instruments, in documents of the time.

9. anon., **Sanctus and Benedictus** (Worcester, Cathedral Library, MS. Add. 68, fragment xxxii).
In spite of its early date, this sentimentally sonorous *Sanctus* displays an uncanny grasp of chording resources and dissonance treatment. The way in which the two upper voices move in relation to the bass line (not one of the standard Sanctus melodies) reflects considerable credit upon the unknown composer, whose penchant for consecutive fifths nicely balanced by phrases in contrary motion contributes no little to the charm of the piece, as to its full yet transparent sound.

10. anon., **Agnus Dei** (Worcester, Cathedral Library, MS. Add. 68, fragment xix *b*). Facsimile: Hughes, *Worcester Mediaeval Harmony*, p. 60.
As this composition has been much mutilated, due to the trimming of the page by some bookbinder of the fifteenth century, bars 1–7, 29–35, and 57–63 have been supplied by conjecture. The plainchant, sung by the tenor, corresponds to the *Agnus Dei* of Mass XV in the Granduale Romanum (Sarum IX). If, as is generally supposed, this plainsong first gained fairly wide currency in the twelfth century, this setting would rank as one of the earliest attempts to adorn it with simple three-part polyphony.

11. anon., **Beata viscera** (Worcester, Cathedral Library, MS. Add. 68, fragment xix *a*).
The text is a trope of the Communion *Beata viscera* (Masses of the B.V.M. from Purification to Advent) whose plainsong is presented in ornate manner in the bass part. The full-sounding harmony results from a generous use of triads, sometimes chords in root position, sometimes in first inversion. The text between *poculo* and *dulcedinis* is almost illegible and a substitute is offered here to conform to the metrical and rhyme schemes.

12. anon., **Alleluia psallat** (Worcester, Cathedral Library, MS. Add. 68, fragment xxxv *k*; Oxford, Bodleian Library, Lat.liturg.d.20, f.25v). Facsimile: Dittmer, *The Worcester Fragments*, plates III/IV.
Most medieval Alleluia settings comprised several sections, the most extended scheme embracing as many as four, of which the first would usually serve as an introduction (making considerable use of voice-exchange) and the second as an elaborated statement of the Alleluia melody. Following these would come two more sections relating to the Alleluia verse. In the case of *Alleluia psallat*, a justly renowned and eminently singable composition, only the first two sections survive. Nevertheless, sufficient clues

remain to show that the verse would almost certainly have been *Virga Jesse*, since the chant of this Alleluia appears in the lowest voice at bar 36. This music belongs to ferial Masses of the B.V.M., and the twin texts of the first section refer to jubilation and joy amidst the sounds of instruments and voices.

The musical material, and of course the texts, are exchanged from voice to voice in typically English manner according to the following pattern (bar 1, and bars 34–35 are outside the scheme):

$$4+4 \ / \ 7+7 \ / \ 5+5$$

In the second section, the lowest voice marks out a constant metrical design:

$$3+3+3+3$$

while the other voices descant freely above it. In view of the brevity of this item, a more extended and contrasting version could be made by the simple expedient of singing *Alleluia psallat* and following it with the plainsong *Alleluia: Virga Jesse* in the *Liber Usualis* (p. 1267). The Alleluia melody before the first incise would not, in this instance, be repeated, since it would already have appeared in the polyphonic version. After the verse has been sung by two or three soloists, and completed by the choir at the words '*ima summis*', the polyphonic *Alleluia psallat* could be repeated, and the plainsong melisma added at the end.

13. anon., **Fulget caelestis curia** (Oxford, Bodleian Library, Lat.liturg.d.20, f.17v/18; New College, MS. 362, f.83v and 90). Facsimile: Hughes, *Worcester Mediæval Harmony*, p. 139.
Manfred Bukofzer transcribed and discussed this rondellus-conductus in his provocative pamphlet *Sumer is icumen in: A Revision* (1944), and it was first performed in this version by way of illustration to a talk, given by Bukofzer, for the BBC Third Programme in 1954. The typical medieval rondellus passed its musical material in regular alternation between all the voice-parts, and in this example bars 1–14 serve as a prelude, and 87–93 as a postlude. The intervening pattern, as far as the music is concerned, appears as follows:

$$c \ a \ b \ f \ d \ e$$
$$b \ c \ a \ e \ f \ d$$
$$a \ b \ c \ d \ e \ f$$

The text, which is about St. Peter, follows an independent exchange scheme of its own. It is interesting to note that a thirteenth-century Customary of St. Peter's, Westminster, gives details of the polyphonic singing of music for the two principal feasts of St. Peter (Feb. 22 and Aug. 1); and while *Fulget* is not mentioned by name it is clear that the use of polyphony was encouraged on these occasions.

14. anon., **Civitas nusquam conditur** (Oxford, New College, MS. 362, f.86v/87). French influence is apparent in the rapid declamatory patterns of the texted voice-parts in this motet in honour of St. Edward, King and Confessor. The tempo should be moderate enough to permit clear and accurate enunciation, and the sustained cantus firmus should not be permitted to overpower the singers. Note the disposition of the sustained notes: 3 bars and 5 bars in alternation, separated always by one bar's

rest. The last nine bars correspond exactly to the first 9 as far as the cantus firmus is concerned, while the other voices correspond only partially to the opening statement.

15. anon., **Ave miles caelestis curiae** (Oxford, Bodleian Library, E Mus. 7, p.x/xi). This motet was first transcribed and discussed in Bukofzer, *Studies in Medieval and Renaissance Music* (1950). The manuscript was written at and for the Benedictine Abbey of St. Edmund at Bury, in Suffolk. In its form and character, the music shares attributes of the motet, rondellus, and conductus. The plainsong basis, moving back and forth between the two instrumental parts, is the antiphon *Ave rex gentis Anglorum*, in honour of St. Edmund, King and Martyr, patron saint of the Abbey. This antiphon is musically identical with the antiphon of the B.V.M. *Ave regina caelorum, mater regis angelorum* (not to be confused with the *Ave regina* sung at the end of Compline). The rondellus element may be seen in the regular exchange of music between the two upper parts on the one hand, and the two lower parts on the other. The preponderance of similar rhythmic movement is reminiscent of the conductus, though the organization of the text—one voice responding to the other—comes closer to the sequence. The proper liturgical place for such a composition may well have been at the end of the service, as a substitute for *Benedicamus Domino*: the upper voices both end with suitable references— '*Benedicamus devote Domino*' and '*dignas laudes referre Domino*'. The solemn and dignified character of the harmonies should not be weakened by too rapid a tempo, and due regard should be given to the climactic effect of the vocal melodic lines, both rising to a high c in their final statement.

16. anon., **Kyrie (Orbis factor)** (Oxford, Bodleian Library, Arch. Selden B 14, f.i). Although other Kyries in the musical fragments of Selden B 14 are provided with tropes, no text is given in this particular setting. The melody of *Orbis factor*, in the Sarum form which differs slightly from the Roman version, is paraphrased in the uppermost voice. The polyphonic sections are best sung by soloists so as to form the maximum contrast with the choral plainsong verses, but if necessary a semichorus could take the place of soloists, when suitable voices are not available.

17. anon., **Gloria in excelsis** (London, British Museum, Sloane MS. 1210, f.138). This conductus setting of the Gloria appears to be freely composed rather than based on plainsong. The first few notes of the uppermost voice are however not unlike the corresponding section of the Gloria No. 3 in the Sarum Gradual, which is here used for the intonation '*Gloria in excelsis Deo*'. Singers in medieval times were expected to know how to produce harmony from a single voice-part, which was sometimes plainsong, sometimes a specially composed non-liturgical melody. In either case, the same technique held good, and the result was a succession of six-three chords, interspersed by octave-and-fifth chords at beginnings and cadences. Much of this extemporized music was never subsequently written down, but it must have sounded similar to the music of this *Gloria*, which should be sung in a deliberate but not inexpressive manner.

18. anon., **Sanctus and Benedictus** (London, Public Record Office, E 149/7/23 dorse). Facsimile: Stevens, *A Recently Discovered English Source of the 14th Century*, in *The Musical Quarterly* xli, Jan. 1955.

This work is one of three polyphonic settings of *Sanctus and Benedictus* written on the back of an Inquisition post mortem which was delivered into the Exchequer in the year 1315. Probably set down in the leisure moments of a musically inclined Exchequer clerk, this music dates from about 1375, and reflects several features of the English church music of that time. The cantus firmus, unadorned, appears in the middle voice (Sarum 4). If suitable solo voices are not available, the music can be performed by a small chorus, but care must be taken to sing the sequential patterns lightly and clearly.

19. anon., **Agnus Dei** (London, Public Record Office, E 149/7/23 dorse). Facsimile: see above, No. 18.
Taken from the same source as the previous item, this *Agnus Dei* is the shortest and simplest of the five settings. The plainsong corresponds to Sarum No. 10 (*Graduale Romanum* XVIII).

20. anon., **Conditor alme siderum** (Oxford, Bodleian Library, Laud lat. 95, f.133v). The hymn melody is freely treated in this setting, and can be seen to stray from one voice to another, a technique known in musicological writings as a 'migrant cantus firmus'. Although the manuscript gives no indication of an *alternatim* performance, this was common practice in the middle ages and survived well into the sixteenth century, when solo verses on the organ replaced polyphonic singing in certain establishments. The polyphonic verses may be sung either by soloists or by a semichorus, though solo performance would be liturgically and historically more correct.

21. anon., **Angelus ad virginem** (Cambridge, University Library, Add. MS. 710, f.124).
The original melody of this Annunciation carol is in the middle voice—the favourite place for a cantus firmus, secular or sacred, in medieval English music. Chaucer mentions the title in his *Canterbury Tales*, and there is evidence of its widespread popularity in another manuscript source (British Museum, Arundel MS. 248, f.154) where the music has a middle English text. The Cambridge setting makes ample and expressive use of faburden—those chains of first inversions so dear to late medieval composers—and also contains occasional flourishes combining eloquence with elegance. Either solo or choral performance is effective.

22. anon., **Deo gracias persolvamus** (Oxford, Bodleian Library, Arch. Selden B.26, f.12). Facsimile: *Early Bodleian Music*, I, pl. lv.
Originally inspired by the preaching of Franciscans, carols successfully intermixed sacred and secular elements in a way that was bound to appeal, yet remain within the bounds of liturgical licence permitted on such feast days as Christmas, the Circumcision, and Epiphany. Many of them appear to have been based on specially written texts embodying the words *Benedicamus Domino* or *Deo gracias*, and from this it seems fairly clear that such carols would have been sung as substitutes for the second *Benedicamus* at Vespers and Matins. This carol, from an early fifteenth-century collection of sacred and secular polyphony, begins each refrain with *Deo gracias*, besides using these words to end the first verse. More important still is the appearance, at the end of the last verse, of *Benedicamus Domino*, which is followed immediately by the response *Deo gracias*

at the beginning of the final singing of the refrain. The small notes for the first tenor in the refrains (called burdens at that time) would in all probability have been extemporized by singers well acquainted with the practice of faburden. Nevertheless, burden and faburden are terms not to be confused. Performance is most effective when a small chorus sings the burden and soloists sing the verses.

23. QUELDRYK, **Gloria** (St. Edmund's College, near Ware; Old Hall Manuscript, f.25v). The Old Hall Manuscript is perhaps the most important liturgical collection of polyphony surviving from medieval England. Long considered to have been written down in the fifteenth century, the manuscript is now thought to belong to the last decade or so of the fourteenth, at least as regards the earliest items in its very extensive repertory. The great majority of this music consists of polyphonic settings for voices alone, or voices and instruments, of the Ordinary of the Mass, but there is also a handful of antiphons and motets.

Before the fourteenth century—indeed throughout the greater part of it—composers remained anonymous, for the simple reason that their creations were intended for local use, and affixing names to them would have served no real purpose. The Old Hall Manuscript, on the other hand, was evidently regarded as a source-book, beautifully written and with some illumination of initial letters, and in fact copies of some of these Mass movements and motets can be seen in later collections. For the first time in English musical history, the names of composers appear with some consistency at the head of each work. Many names have been found in documents connected with the Chapel Royal, for whose use the manuscript may originally have been compiled.

Nothing is known of Queldryk, though he may have taken his name from an estate at Fountains in Yorkshire, where the Cistercian Abbey resounded with polyphonic singing, in spite of the strictness of its rule. The structure of his *Gloria* is reminiscent of *Ave miles caelestis curiae* (No. 15), with its four-part harmony made up of two instrumental parts and two superimposed vocal parts which declaim in alternation and fill in with textless melismata. Yet there are also differences, for here the voices do not exchange melodic material. There is a continuous new invention, in spite of the fact that the two lower lines repeat themselves at bar 37, in note-values reduced by half. This was a common feature of isorhythmic practice, and served to establish a solid formal basis upon which the composer could build his decorative vocal lines. Queldryk favours the rapid declamation of the French motet, and allows the voices to combine with text only at important points—the beginning of the trope, the '*miserere nobis*', and the '*Amen*'. Although solo performance was almost certainly the composer's original intention, he would have tolerated opposing semichoruses of well-blended voices in the alto range. The instrumental parts can be played on the organ, but they sound well on cor anglais and bassoon, or viola and cello. The work cannot, unfortunately, be used liturgically as it contains the trope *Spiritus et alme* (for Masses of the B.V.M.) and this, like all other tropes, is forbidden in the Catholic Church today.

24. JOHN EXCETRE, **Sanctus and Benedictus** (St. Edmund's College, near Ware; Old Hall Manuscript, f.99).

Excetre was a member of the Chapel Royal from approximately 1374 until 1396, and his surname (as in many similar cases) probably shows the town of his origin. Only three works by him have been preserved for posterity: a *Gloria*, a *Credo*, and this *Sanctus and Benedictus*, all of them belonging stylistically to the last quarter of the fourteenth century. This setting is not based on plainsong, but on a non-liturgical cantus firmus written down among other monophonic pieces (in mensural notation) on the flyleaves of a Sarum Gradual in the British Museum (Lansdowne 462). These melodic sources were referred to in later documents as squares, because of the shape of their notation. Solo or choral performance is possible.

25. OLYVER, **Agnus Dei** (St. Edmund's College, near Ware; Old Hall Manuscript f.108v).

Nothing is known of Olyver, but the style of his music suggests that he wrote his Mass settings (*Credo*; two *Sanctus*; *Agnus Dei*) towards the close of the fourteenth century. His *Agnus Dei*, whose alto part consists of a freely decorated version of Sarum 6 (*Graduale Romanum* II), may be compared to a variation sequence, since each of the three plainsong invocations consists of the same music. Not only is the uppermost melody varied; so too is the metre and the harmony. Solo or choral performance is possible.

26. THOMAS DAMETT, **Beata Dei genetrix** (St. Edmund's College, near Ware; Old Hall Manuscript, f.39v).

Damett was appointed rector of the parish church of Stockton (Wiltshire) in 1413, when he was about twenty-five years of age. Nothing is known of his early musical training, but he was already a clerk of the Chapel Royal at the time of his Stockton appointment, and later enjoyed various preferments such as that of the prebend of Rugmere in St. Paul's, the patron being King Henry V, and another prebend in St. George's Chapel, Windsor. He died in 1437, his will being proved on April 14 of that year.

Nine works by Damett testify to his unusual musical skill, which embraced relatively simple conductus settings of Mass sections and, at the other end of the scale, a complex isorhythmic motet in honour of Henry V and St. George. His *Beata Dei genetrix* sets a processional antiphon, sung before Mass or Vespers of the B.V.M., in alternating two- and three-part harmony. This was almost certainly intended for unequal forces: soloists would sing the duets, and a small chorus the three-part sections.

27. LEONEL POWER, **Ave Regina caelorum** (St. Edmund's College, near Ware; Old Hall Manuscript, f.36).

Power, who belongs to a group of English composers most of whose music is preserved in continental sources, spent at least the last twenty years of his life at Canterbury. From 1441 until his death in 1445 his name appears among the livery lists of Christ Church, Canterbury, as one of the more important of the laymen, and he may possibly have been master of the children. This setting of one of the four great antiphons of the B.V.M. should not be confused with his *Ave regina caelorum, mater regis angelorum*, known from manuscripts at Oxford, Trent, and Bologna. The plainsong, in lightly decorated form, lies in the middle voice-part. By Power's time, it was becoming more and more fashionable to use more than one voice to a part when singing works of this kind; nevertheless performance by soloists is perfectly feasible.

28. JOHN DUNSTABLE, **Veni Sancte Spiritus** (St. Edmund's College, near Ware; Old Hall Manuscript, f.55v; Trent, Castel del Buon Consiglio, MS. 92, 1537; Modena, Biblioteca Estense, MS.∝.X.1.11, f.106v; Aosta, Biblioteca del Seminario, MS. without shelfmark, f.274v; Munich, Staatsbibliothek, MS. 3224, f.30v). Facsimile: Hinrichsen Edition 1453, frontispiece.

The known facts about Dunstable's career seem to be in inverse proportion to his fame as a composer. He was a member of the Duke of Bedford's private chapel, and served abroad during the time when the Duke acted as Regent in France. From 1419 until 1440, Dunstable held a canonry at Hereford, but since this was essentially an absentee benefice he pursued his career on the continent of Europe, where in fact most of his compositions are still to be found. *Veni Sancte Spiritus* is unusual in that it does appear in an English source, but without the composer's name, indicating perhaps that he was better known abroad than at home. Dunstable died in 1453, on Christmas Eve, and he was buried in the church of St. Stephen Walbrook in the City of London. His complete works were transcribed and edited by Manfred Bukofzer for *Musica Britannica* VIII, this volume appearing most aptly in 1953, on the five-hundredth anniversary of the composer's death.

Veni Sancte Spiritus reveals the ingenious craftsmanship of its composer, and at the same time his unerring control of music as sheer sound. Although cast in the strict mould of an isorhythmic motet, the aural impression received is one of great freedom combined with gradually increasing harmonic tension. This is partly due to the successive shortening of note-values in the lowest part, which begins by stating its melody (the second and third lines of the hymn *Veni Creator*) in long-sustained notes, best played on the organ or by trombones. The rhythmic pattern of this opening section (bars 1–55) is then repeated (46–90), and it is worth noticing that not just the tenor, but all the other voices follow the prescribed pattern although they now present different music. In the second section, where the time-signature changes to 3/2, this twofold repetition may once again be observed, this time to a new rhythmic scheme. The one exception is the lowest part, which states its melodic material as before, but reduces the proportion of the note-values from 9 to 6. In the final (3/4) section, this is still further reduced from 6 to 3, and the effect is inevitably one of accelerated harmonic rhythm and final emergence of the melody as part of the hymn-tune.

The texts suggest a comparable degree of subtlety, for the soprano part carries the text of the sequence *Veni Sancte Spiritus* but the melody (paraphrased) of the hymn *Veni Creator*. The alto sings a poem related to the sequence in thought and metre, while the tenor sings the words (but not the tune) of the hymn. Both hymn and sequence belong to the liturgy of Whitsunday.

29. JOHN DUNSTABLE, **Regina caeli laetare** (Aosta, Biblioteca del Seminario, MS. without shelfmark, f.191v; also manuscripts at Bologna, Florence, and Munich). This antiphon, sung after Compline from Easter until Trinity in honour of the B.V.M., displays Dunstable's mastery of the technique of melodic paraphrase, for the plain-

song appears in the uppermost part in a delicately ornamented form, its floating rhythms carrying the text along in an unhurried yet passionate paean of praise. The lower parts are best assigned to organ or instrumentalists (violas, for instance) except at the two Alleluias, where tenor voices are needed. The instruments and voices can double each other at these points.

30. JOHN DUNSTABLE, **Quam pulchra es** (Bologna, Bibl. Univ. MS. 2216, p.84; Bologna, Conservatorio G. B. Martini, MS. Q.15, f.284v, also five other manuscripts). One of Dunstable's most famous works, this processional antiphon for Vespers and Mass of the B.V.M. does not rely on plainsong in any of its three voices, which unite in rhythm and declamation in such a way that the older conductus style is wedded to a new treatment of text—the natural rhythm of the words is respected, as is the general sense of their meaning. The words of the Song of Songs clearly inspired Dunstable to indulge in a lyrical effusion of unusual and unprecedented warmth. While choral performance is eminently suitable, this music is by no means excluded from solo rendition.

31. anon., **Gloria, laus et honor** (London, British Museum, Egerton MS. 3307, f.10v).
The prose for Palm Sunday procession, *Gloria, laus et honor*, was traditionally sung by seven choirboys stationed in some lofty eminence inside the church, but with the advent of polyphonic settings the boys may have been joined by a trio of singers who took care of the verses in harmony. Modern performances may follow this custom; or if more contrast and variety of tone is needed, the chorus can sing the first and last verses (*Gloria, laus*), soloists the middle verses, and all trebles or sopranos the recurring plain-song refrain. Although ornamented phrases from the plainsong appear from time to time in the polyphonic verses, these are to a large extent freely composed.

32. WALTER FRYE, **Salve Virgo Mater** (Trent, Castello del Buon Consiglio, MS. 88, f.70).
Although Frye joined a London guild of musicians in 1456, it seems that like Dunstable and certain other English composers of the mid-fifteenth century, he chose to spend the greater part of his career on the continent. Only one motet by Frye survives in an English source, though many of his other compositions, both sacred and secular, found their way into anthologies copied for continental courts and chapels. The motet *Salve Virgo* (attributed to Frye by Bukofzer) is based on the plainsong tenor *Summae Trinitatis*, the ninth respond at Matins of Trinity Sunday. From this motet the composer derived a Mass *Summae Trinitatis*, the two compositions being inter-related not only by the plainsong but also by correspondences in musical material. If the motet is performed by a choir, the passage from bar 39 (*'redemit Christus'* in the upper two voices) to bar 78 (*'Gentibus'* in the bass part) may be sung by soloists or semichorus.

33. WILLIAM CORNYSH, **Ave Maria Mater Dei** (Eton College, MS. 178, f.x4).
Cornysh, who served as Master of the Children of the Chapel Royal from 1509 until

1523, was the most outstanding member of a musical family and a composer of considerable versatility. Besides his motets and settings of the Magnificat, he also wrote works with an English text, such as the moving Passiontide carol *Woefully arrayed*. His *Ave Maria Mater Dei*, a votive antiphon in honour of the B.V.M., is an example of the kind of music that would have been sung by choirs and city guilds of musicians at the close of Compline, as a form of popular devotion to the Virgin. The motet should be performed by a male voice choir, and all the sections whose text appears in italics should be sung by soloists.

34. ROBERT FAYRFAX, **Magnificat ('Regale')** (London, Lambeth Palace MS. 1, No. 16; Cambridge, Gonville & Caius College MS. 667; Oxford, Bodleian Library, Lat.liturg.a.9, f.5; Cambridge, Peterhouse MSS. 40, 41, 31, 32; Cambridge. Univ. Lib. Dd.xiii.27 and St. John's College 234; British Museum Add.MS. 34191, f.45).
Fayrfax was born in 1464, and died in 1521, the year of Josquin's death. As a Gentleman of the Chapel Royal, he served under Henry VII and Henry VIII, reaching the climax of his career in 1520, when he directed the English choir in the ceremonies of the Field of the Cloth of Gold. His provincial post was that of organist at St. Alban's Abbey. The Masses, motets, and Magnificats of Fayrfax reveal him as one of the most distinguished choral composers of his generation, and there is scarcely a work of his that does not reflect the dignity and grandeur of Chapel Royal singing under his leadership. His *Magnificat 'Regale'* (not related musically to his *Mass 'Regali ex progenie'*) is based on a freely elaborated faburden of the eighth tone of the Magnificat, and this appears in the tenor part throughout. To obtain his faburden, Fayrfax transposed the chant (using the 'c' ending) down a fifth, then wrote above it a derived melody maintaining the interval of a sixth, except at beginnings and endings where the octave is used. This derived melody is the faburden, and the reason for its preference may lie in the greater number of disjunct intervals, especially fourths, as opposed to the original tone with its mainly conjunct motion. In performance, the word '*Magnificat*' should be intoned by a solo voice, and all the other plainsong assigned to a group of mens' voices. The polyphony can either be sung full throughout, or if desired the duets, trios, and quartets can be sung by soloists.

35. ROBERT CARVER, **Gaude flore virginali** (Edinburgh, National Library of Scotland, Adv.MS. 5.1.15, No. 8).
Carver, a canon of Scone Abbey, was one of Scotland's foremost composers of liturgical music in the early part of the sixteenth century. All of his music is contained in one choirbook at Edinburgh, and although this may not be in the composer's own hand, it was certainly used for services in Scone Abbey. Some of his works possess unusual features, such as the *Missa L'homme armé*, the only known Mass on this popular theme by a non-continental composer; and the motet *O bone Jesu* whose full sections are written in 19-part polyphony. His *Gaude flore virginali*, on the other hand, conforms largely to the scope and design of other works on this text by Carver's contemporaries in England. Further information on the manuscript, the composer, and the music may be found in *Musica Disciplina* XIII (1959) p. 155, and in *Robert Carver: Omnia Opera* I (American Institute of Musicology).

36. JOHN TAVERNER, **Agnus Dei** (from '*The Western Wind*' Mass). (Oxford, Bodleian Library, MS. Mus.e.1–5; London, British Museum, Add.MS. 17802–5). Taverner's early training was at the collegiate church of Tattershall in Lincolnshire, and the latter part of his life was spent at Boston. His only significant excursion from his native environment was a period of several years at Cardinal College, Oxford (now Christ Church), where he served as the first organist and *informator choristarum*. His extant music, which comprises eight Masses, three settings of Magnificat, a *Te Deum*, five responsories, and some two dozen motets and fragments of Masses, affords ready proof of great contrapuntal skill combined with a feeling for choral balance that could only have come from years of singing, as boy and man, in the choirs of Tattershall and Oxford. His Mass on the secular tune *The Western Wind* is the earliest known work of its kind in England, and though continental composers had freely availed themselves of the secular repertory long before Taverner's time, it was he who developed to a high degree the technique of variation which can be found throughout this work. The tune of *The Western Wind* is stated thirty-six times in all, and each of the four movements enjoys an equal number of statements. The nine in *Agnus Dei* are arranged in three groups of three, in order to conform with the threefold invocation of the liturgical text. Those sections scored for two or three voices may be sung by soloists, or by a semi-chorus, as may seem most convenient for the size of the choir and the building in which they sing.

37. JOHN TAVERNER, **Magnificat** (London, British Museum, Add.MS. 17802–5). A fair proportion of early liturgical music written in England was intended for mens' voices, the counter-tenor (or mean) voice sustaining the uppermost part while tenors, baritones, and basses filled out the texture with sonorous harmony or sturdy counter-point. An Italian visitor, writing at the time when Taverner was still a young man, bestowed especial praise on the quality and depth of the bass voices of the Chapel Royal; and although choirboys too are occasionally mentioned with approval in letters and documents of Tudor times, it can hardly be doubted that the men's voices were capable of providing a remarkably sure foundation to the choral tone as a whole, and equally capable of performing as a group in their own right. This setting of Tone 6 displays many features of Taverner's mature work, and may still have been sung as late as the reign of Mary I. The antiphonal effect is best achieved by using two distinct semichoruses, placed well apart from each other.

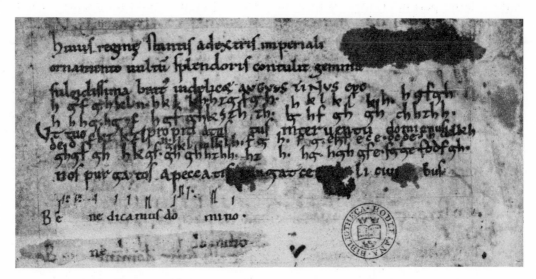

Ut tuo propitiatus, verse of the responsory *Sancte Dei pretiose*
(Oxford, Bodleian Library, MS. Bodley 572, fol. 49v.)

1. SANCTE DEI PRETIOSE

Transcribed and edited by
DENIS STEVENS

ANON., *c.* 1100
Oxford, Bodleian Library, MS. Bodley 572

San - cte _____ De - - - - - i ____ pre - ti -
- o - - - - se __ pro - to - mar - tyr _____ Ste -
- pha - - - ne, __ qui ____ vir - tu - - - te ____ ca - ri -
- ta - - - tis __ cir - cum - ful - tus _____
un - di - - que: Do - - mi - num pro i - ni - mi -
- co ex - o - - ra - sti po - - - pu - lo.
Fun - de __ pre - - - ces pro _____ de - vo - -
- to ti - bi __ nunc col - - - - - - - - - - -
- - - - - - - - - - - - - le - gi - o. __

N.B. Bar 8, lower voice, last note reads A, but the B flat appears in plainsong sources.

2. ALLELUIA: POST PARTUM

Transcribed and edited by
FRANK LL. HARRISON

ANON., *c.* 1225
Wolfenbüttel, Ducal Library, MS 677

c

-i - ge - ni - - - trix _____

in - ter - ce - de pro no - bis. _____

Al - - le - - lu -

- ia. _____

3. PERSPICE CHRISTICOLA

Transcribed and edited by
DENIS STEVENS

ANON., *c.* 1270
London, British Museum, Harley MS 978

Per - spi - ce Chri - sti - co - la _____ quae dig - na - ti - o

Cae - li - cus a - gri - co - la pro vi - tis vi - ti - o.

Fi - li - o non par - cens ex - po - su - it mor -

-tis ex - i - ti - o; Qui cap - ti - vos se - mi - vi - vos

a sup - pli - ci - o Vi - tae do - nat _____

et se - cum co - ro - nat in cae - li so - li - o.

PES

This canon may be sung by 2, 3 or 4 voices; the first begins together with those who sing (or play) the PES, and successive voices enter as the third bar is reached. Sing the PES to '0'; and let the canon end (after the desired number of repetitions) when the *leading* voice reaches the word 'solio'

4. MILES CHRISTI GLORIOSE

Transcribed and edited by
JEREMY NOBLE

ANON., *c.* 1200
London, Westminster Abbey, MS 33327

*The change from the free rhythm of the plainsong to the measured pulse of the motet should be imperceptible.

-a de - co - ra - tur et lae - ta - tur cae - li cu - ri -

san - cti - ta - tis, iu - bar ho - ne - sta - tis

(a) -

-a: qui vi - tae me - ri - ta per lau - da -

qui mun - da - nis o - pi - bus pe - de re - pu - di - a -

(a) -

-bi - li - a iam in po - li re - gnas glo - ri - a.

-sti: es Chri - sti__ ve - sti - gi - a to - ta men - te

(a) - - - - - - - -

Nunc ec - cle - si - a mi - li - tans in tu - a lau - de

per - se - cu - tus ab in - fan - ci - a per vi - am__

(a) - - - - - - - - -

Chri - sto dat prae - co - ni - a dul - ci - a, ut tu -

pau - per - ta - tis at - que san - cte ca - ri - ta - tis,

(a) -

-o pro - pi - ti - a - tu li - be - re - tur a re - a - tu

iam in re - gno cla - ri - ta - tis_ re - do - lens su - a - vi -

(a) -

5. EPIPHANIAM DOMINO CANAMUS

Transcribed and edited by
DENIS STEVENS

ANON., c 1310
Montpellier, Bibl. Univ. H.196; also
Oxford, New College MS. 362

I: In som - nis hos mo - net an - ge - lus, ne re - de - ant ad
II: Pa - ve - bat et - e - nim ni - mi - um re - gem na - tum, ve -

re - gem com - mo - tum pro - pter reg - na. Ma - gi stel - la
-rens a - mit - te - re reg - ni iu - ra. Qui per - cus - sus

si - bi mi - can - te prae vi - a, per - gunt a - la - cres
cor - da ni - mi - um prae i - ra, ex tem - plo man - dat

i - ti - ne - ra, pa - tri - am quae e - os du - ce - bat
e - lu - di - a ma - gi - ca non lin - qui ta - li - ter

ad pro - pri - am, lin - quen - tes He - ro - dis man - da - ta.
im - pu - ni - ta, sed mox pri - va - ri e - os vi - ta.

Om - nis nunc ca - ter - va tin - nu - lum iun - gat lau - di - bus or -
Mis - ti - ce of - fer - ens re - gi re - gum Chri - sto mu - ne - ra____

FULL CHOIR

-ga - ni neu - ma. Pos - cens ut per or - bem reg - na om - ni - a
pre - ti - o - sa.

pro - te - gat in sae - cu - la sem - pi - ter - na. A - men.____

6. SALVE SANCTA PARENS

(INTROIT)

Transcribed and edited by
DENIS STEVENS

ANON., *c.* 1290
Worcester Cathedral Library Add. 68

D

7. ALLELUIA-PER TE DEI GENETRIX

Transcribed and edited by
DENIS STEVENS

ANON., *c.* 1300
Oxford, Bodleian Library, Lat. liturg. d. 20

ful - gens, so - lem la - ten - tem sub nu - be - cu - la mi - rae su - sce-

tu per vo - cem an - ge - li - cam Chri - stum con - ce - pi - sti

et mun do ge-

-pi - sti et in tu - a cel - lu - la mun - do ge - nu - i - sti

fe - rens es - cam mel - li - cam, hu - ic mun - do tri - sti, quem vir - go ge - nu - i - sti

(e) - nu - i - sti

CHOIR

sal - va - to - rem.

(e)

(e)

8. CANDENS LILIUM COLUMBINA

Transcribed and edited by
DENIS STEVENS

ANON., *c.* 1300
Oxford, Bodleian Library, Lat. liturg. d. 20
Cambridge, Pembroke College, MS. 228

9. SANCTUS AND BENEDICTUS

Transcribed and edited by
DENIS STEVENS

ANON., *c.* 1310
Worcester, Cathedral Library, Add. MS. 68

10. AGNUS DEI

Transcribed and edited by
DENIS STEVENS

ANON., *c.* 1310
Worcester, Cathedral Library, Add. MS. 68

11. BEATA VISCERA

Transcribed and edited by
DENIS STEVENS

ANON., *c.* 1290
Worcester, Cathedral Library, MS. Add. 68

12. ALLELUIA PSALLAT

Transcribed and edited by
DENIS STEVENS

ANON., *c.* 1290
Oxford, Bodleian Library, Lat. liturg. d. 20
also Worcester, Cathedral Library Add. MS. 68

13. FULGET CAELESTIS CURIA

Transcribed and edited by
MANFRED BUKOFZER

ANON., *c.* 1310
Oxford, Bodleian Library, Lat. liturg. d. 20;
also Oxford, New College MS. 362

Reprinted from SUMER IS ICUMEN IN: A Revision by M. Bukofzer, by permission of the University of
California Press

14. CIVITAS NUSQUAM CONDITUR

Transcribed and edited by
MANFRED BUKOFZER

ANON., *c.* 1325
Oxford, New College MS. 362

-bro fi - gi - tur tri-bu-at ut lu - cem

-ri cum san - ctis lae-ti-ci - am; qui - a

ca - li - gi - no - so po - pu - lo. Quo-ni - am qui ca - ret

con - so - nat et re - do - let me - li - us iun - ctu -

lu - mi - ne nes - cit quo ten-dat i - ti - ne - re; aut

-ra bo - no - rum me - ri - to hic

res - pon - det in cen - tu - plo. et i - de -

gau - di - um, pre - ci - bus cu - ius

-o si - bi con - ce - di - tur glo - ri - a quo nun-quam de -

per - du - ca - mur ad e - o - rum con -

-fi - ci - et lae - ti - ci - a per in - fi - ni - ta sae - cu - la.

-sor - ti - um quo ma - ne - bunt in per - pe - tu - um.

15. AVE MILES CAELESTIS CURIAE

Transcribed and edited by
MANFRED BUKOFZER

ANON., *c.* 1340
Oxford, Bodleian Library, E. Mus. 7

A - ve mi - les cae - le - stis cu - ri - ae quem de - co - rat ho-

-nor vic - to - ri - ae vi - vis De - o fru - ens re - qui - e mo-

By permission of J. M. Dent & Sons, Ltd.

16. KYRIE (ORBIS FACTOR)

Transcribed and edited by
DENIS STEVENS

ANON., *c.* 1380
Oxford, Bodleian Library, Arch. Selden B.14

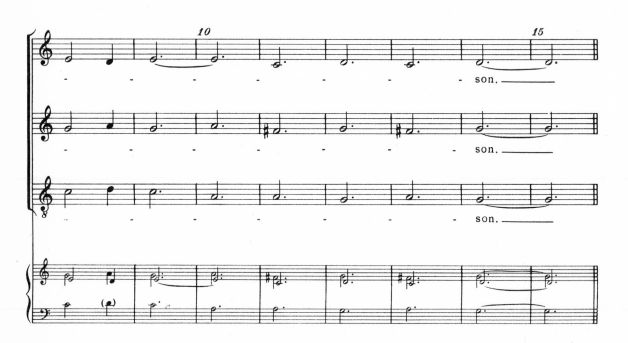

TENORS and BASSES

Ky - ri - e e - lei - - - son.

Ky - ri - e e - lei - - -

Ky - ri - e e - lei - - -

Ky - ri - e (e) - lei - - -

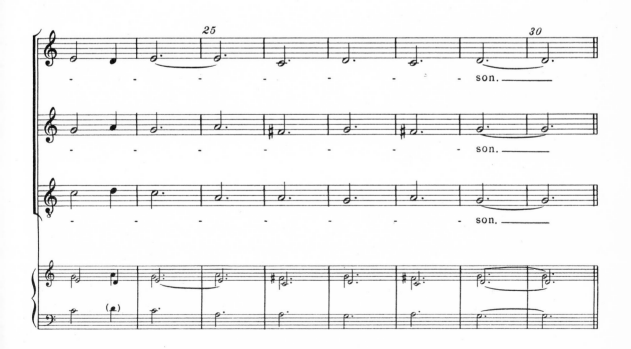

- - - - - - son.

- - - - - son.

- - - - - son.

Chri - ste _____ e - lei - - son.

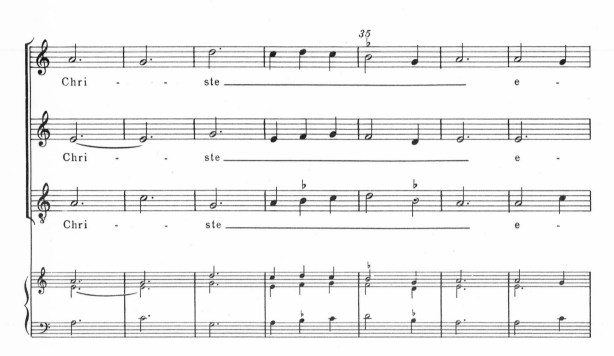

Chri - ste _____ e -

Chri - ste _____ e -

Chri - ste _____ e -

-lei - - - - - - - son. _____

-lei - - - - - - - son. _____

-lei - - - - - - - son. _____

17. GLORIA IN EXCELSIS

Transcribed and edited by
JEREMY NOBLE

ANON., *c.* 1350
British Museum, Sloane MS. 1210

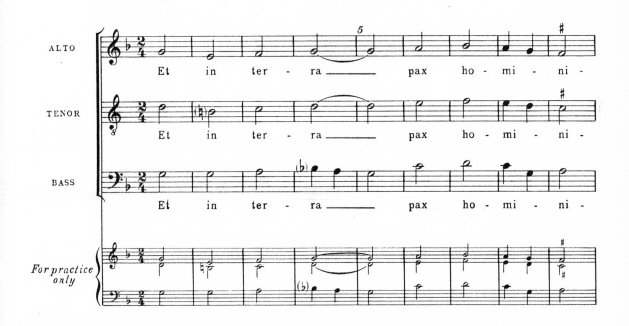

glo - ri - fi - ca - mus te,

glo - ri - fi - ca - mus te,

glo - ri - fi - ca - mus te,

gra - ci - as a - gi - mus ti - - -

gra - ci - as a - gi - mus ti - - -

gra - ci - as a - gi - mus ti - - -

-bi prop-ter ma-gnam glo - ri - am tu -

-bi prop-ter ma-gnam glo - ri - am tu -

-bi prop-ter ma-gnam glo - ri - am tu -

G

18. SANCTUS AND BENEDICTUS

Transcribed and edited by
DENIS STEVENS

ANON., *c.* 1375
London, Public Record Office E 149/7/23

-ctus _____ Do - mi - nus

-ctus _____ Do - mi - nus

-ctus _____ Do - mi - nus

De - us _____ Sa -

De - us _____ Sa -

De - us _____ Sa -

-ba - oth, ple - ni

-ba - oth, ple - ni _____

-ba - oth, ple - ni _____

19. AGNUS DEI

Transcribed and edited by
DENIS STEVENS

ANON., *c.* 1375
London, Public Record Office E 119/7/23

ALTO

1. A - gnus De — - i, qui tol - lis pec - ca-
3. A - gnus De — - i, qui tol - lis pec - ca-

TENOR

1. A - gnus De — - i, qui tol - lis pec - ca-
3. A - gnus De — - i, qui tol - lis pec - ca-

TENOR

1. A - gnus De — - i, qui tol - lis pec - ca-
3. A - gnus De — - i, qui tol - lis pec - ca-

For practice only

-ta ___ mun - di, mi - se - re - re no - bis.
-ta ___ mun - di, do - na ___ no - bis pa - cem.

-ta mun - di, mi - se - re - re no - bis.
-ta mun - di, do - na no - bis pa - cem.

-ta mun - di, mi - se - re - re no - bis.
-ta mun - di, do - na no - bis pa - cem.

2. A - gnus De - i, qui tol - lis pec - ca - ta mun - di, mi - se - re - re no - bis.

20. CONDITOR ALME SIDERUM

Transcribed and edited by
DENIS STEVENS

ANON., *c.* 1400
Oxford, Bodleian Library, MS. Laud lat. 95

1 Con - di - tor al - me si - de - rum, Ae - ter - na lux cre - den - ti - um,

Chri - ste re - demp - tor om - ni - um, Ex - au - di pre - ces sup - pli - cum.

ALTO

2 Qui con - do - lens in - te - ri - tu Mor - tis pe -

TENOR

2 Qui con - do - lens in - te - ri - tu Mor - tis pe -

BASS

2 Qui con - do - lens in - te - ri - tu Mor - tis pe -

For practice only

- ri - re sae - cu - lum, Sal - va - sti mun - dum

- ri - re sae - cu - lum, Sal - va - sti mun - dum

- ri - re sae - cu - lum, Sal - va - sti mun - dum

H

lan - gui - dum, Do - nans re - is re - me - di - um.

lan - gui - dum, Do - nans re - is re - me - di - um.

lan - gui - dum, Do - nans re - is re - me - di - um.

3 Ver - gen - te mun - di ve - spe - re, U - ti spon - sus de tha - la - mo,

E - gres - sus ho - ne - stis - si - ma Vir - gi - nis ma - tris clau - su - la.

4 Cu - jus for - ti ____ po - ten - ti - ae Ge - nu cur -

4 Cu - jus for - ti po - ten - ti - ae Ge - nu cur -

4 Cu - jus for - ti ____ po - ten - ti - ae Ge - nu cur -

-van - tur__ om - ni - a,__ Cae - le - sti - a, ter -

-van - tur__ om - ni - a, Cae - le - sti - a, ter -

-van - tur__ om - ni - a, Cae - le - sti - a, ter -

-re - stri - a, Nu - tu fa - ten - tur__ sub - di - ta.

-re - stri - a, Nu - tu fa - ten - tur sub - di - ta.

-re - stri - a, Nu - tu fa - ten - tur__ sub - di - ta.

5 Te de - pre - ca - mur a - gi - e, Ven - tu - re ju - dex sae - cu - li,

Con - ser - va nos in tem - po - re Ho - stis a te - lo per - fi - di.

21. ANGELUS AD VIRGINEM

Transcribed and edited by
DENIS STEVENS

ANON., 14th century
Cambridge, University Library, Add. 710

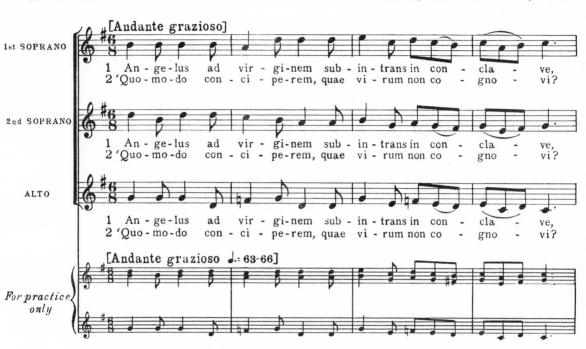

Reprinted by permission of Novello & Co., Ltd.

22. DEO GRACIAS PERSOLVAMUS

Transcribed and edited by
JOHN STEVENS

ANON., *c.* 1430
Oxford, Bodleian Library, Arch. Selden B.26

By permission of the Royal Musical Association and the Editorial Committee of 'Musica Britannica'

23. GLORIA

Transcribed and edited by
DENIS STEVENS

QUELDRYK
Old Hall MS., c. 1400

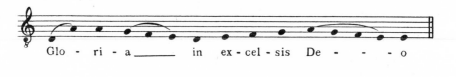

24. SANCTUS AND BENEDICTUS

Transcribed and edited by
DENIS STEVENS

JOHN EXCETRE
Old Hall MS., c. 1400

25. AGNUS DEI

Transcribed and edited by
DENIS STEVENS

OLYVER
Old Hall MS., *c.* 1400

26. BEATA DEI GENETRIX

Transcribed and edited by
DENIS STEVENS

THOMAS DAMETT(? – 1437)
Old Hall MS.

For practice only

27. AVE REGINA CAELORUM

Transcribed and edited by
DENIS STEVENS

LEONEL POWER (? –1445)
Old Hall MS.

III

28. VENI SANCTE SPIRITUS

JOHN DUNSTABLE (?—1453)
Old Hall MS.
Trento, Castel del Buon Consiglio, MS. 92
Modena, Biblioteca Estense, ɑ X 1,11

Transcribed and edited by
DENIS STEVENS

29. REGINA CAELI LAETARE

Transcribed and edited by
MANFRED BUKOFZER

JOHN DUNSTABLE (?-1453)
Aosta, Seminario
Modena, Biblioteca Estense, αX 1, 11

ORGAN
or
INSTRUMENTS

*For practice
only*

By permission of the Royal Musical Association and the Editorial Committee of 'Musica Britannica'

30. QUAM PULCHRA ES

Transcribed and edited by
MANFRED BUKOFZER

JOHN DUNSTABLE (?-1453)
Bologna, Bibl. Univ. MS. 2216; also
Bologna, Conservatorio G. B. Martini, MS. Q 15

By permission of the Royal Musical Association and the Editorial Committee of 'Musica Britannica'

31. GLORIA, LAUS ET HONOR

Transcribed and edited by
GWYNN S. McPEEK

ANON., c. 1460
British Museum, Egerton MS. 3307

By permission of the Oxford University Press

134

CHORUS

Glo - ri - a,— laus_ et ho-nor___ ti-bi sit, rex Chri-ste re-demp-

-tor, Cu - i pu-e - ri-le___ de - cus prom-psit_ O-san-na_ pi-um.

ALTO SOLO

Coe - - - tus_____ in _____

TENOR SOLO

Coe - - - tus_____ in _____

BASS SOLO

Coe - - - tus_____ in_____

ex - - - - - cel - - sis

ex - - - - - cel - sis _____

ex - - - - cel - - sis _____

32. SALVE VIRGO MATER

Transcribed and edited by
SYLVIA W. KENNEY

WALTER FRYE (c. 1480)
Trent MS. 88

By permission of Dr. Armen Carapetyan, Director of the American Institute of Musicology

33. AVE MARIA MATER DEI

Transcribed and edited by
FRANK Ll. HARRISON

WILLIAM CORNYSH (?-1523)
Eton Choirbook

34. MAGNIFICAT ('Regale')

Transcribed and edited by
FRANK LL. HARRISON

ROBERT FAYRFAX (1464–1521)
The Eton Choirbook

sa - lu - ta - - - ri_____ me____ o.

____ sa - lu - ta - ri_____ me - ____ o.

-o sa - lu - ta - ri__ me - ____ o.

sa - lu - ta - ri me - - - - o.

- lu - ta - ri_____ me - - o.

Qui - a re - spe - xit hu - mi - li - ta - tem an - cil - lae su - ae:

ec - ce e - nim ex hoc be - a - tam me di - cent o - mnes ge - ne - ra - ti - o - nes.

TREBLE

Qui - - - - a_____

TENOR

Qui - - - - a____ fe - -

BASS

Qui - - - a fe - -

Et mi-se - ri-cor-di-a e-ius a pro-ge-ni-e— in— pro-ge - ni-es ti-men-ti-bus e-um.

TREBLE

Fe - cit po-ten - ti - am ____

MEAN

Fe - - cit po-ten - ti - am

COUNTER-TENOR

Fe - - cit po - ten-ti - am ____ in — bra-

TENOR

Fe - - cit po-ten - ti - am in

BASS

Fe - cit po-ten - - ti - am in

in bra - chi - o _____ su - o:

in bra - - chi-o su - - - o: ____

- chi - - o su - - - o: dis-

bra - chi - o _____ su - - o:

bra - chi - - - - o su - o: dis -

De-po-su - it po-ten - tes___ de se - de, et ex-al-ta-vit hu-mi-les.

MEAN

E - su - ri - en -

COUNTER-
TENOR

E - su - ri - en - - - - - tes

TENOR

E - su - ri - - en -

BASS

E - su - ri - - - en - - tes

- tes___ im - ple - - - - - -

im - ple - - - - - - -

- tes im - ple - -

im - ple - -

Glo - ri - a Pa - tri, et Fi - li - o, et Spi - ri - tu - i San - cto.

TREBLE

195

Sic - ut

BASS

Sic - ut e - rat

200

e - rat in prin - ci

in prin - ci - pi

205

- pi

TREBLE

210

-o,

MEAN

et nunc et

COUNTER-
TENOR

et nunc et

TENOR

et nunc et sem -

BASS

-o,

35. GAUDE FLORE VIRGINALI

Transcribed and edited by
DENIS STEVENS

ROBERT CARVER (*c.* 1191–after 1546)
Edinburgh, National Library, Adv. MS. 5/1/15

o

36. AGNUS DEI

From 'THE WESTERN WIND' MASS

Transcribed and edited by
PHILIP BRETT

JOHN TAVERNER (c. 1495–1545)

By permission of Stainer & Bell, Ltd.

37. MAGNIFICAT

Transcribed and edited by
EDMUND HARDING

JOHN TAVERNER (*c.* 1495-1545)

Ma - gni - fi - cat a - ni - ma me - a ___ Do - mi - num

1st TENOR

2nd TENOR

1st BASS

2nd BASS

For practice only

Qui - a re - spe - xit hu - mi - li - ta - tem an - cill - ae su - ae: ec - ce e -
- nim ex hoc be - a - tam me di - cent om - nes ge - ne - ra - ti - o - nes.
2nd T
1st B
2nd B
35
Qui - a fe - - - - - - - - - cit mi -
Qui - - - - a fe - - - - cit
40
- hi ma - - gna qui po - tens
mi - hi ma - - - gna qui po - tens
mi - hi ma - - - gna qui po -
45
50
qui po - tens est:
qui po - tens est:
- tens est, qui po - tens est:

De-po-su-it po-ten-tes_ de se-de:_ et ex-al-ta-vit_ hu-mi-les.

E - su-ri-en - - - tes, e - su-ri-

E - su-ri-en - tes, e - su-ri -

E - su-ri-en - - - - tes,

-en - tes, e - su-ri-en - - - tes

-en - tes, e - su-ri-en - tes

e - su-ri - en - tes im-ple-vit

im - ple-vit bo -

im-ple-vit bo - - - - - -

bo - - - - -

in sae-cu - - la, saecu - la.

sae - cu - - la, in sae - - cu-la.

-ius in _____ sae - cu - la. _____

- - la, in sae-cu - - la.

Glo-ri - a Pa - tri, _ et Fi - li - o: _ et Spi - ri - tu - i _ Sanc - to.

Sic - - ut e - - - - - - -

Sic - - ut _ e - -

- -rat in _ prin - ci - pi - - - - - -

- -rat in _ prin - ci - pi - - - - - -

TRANSLATIONS

1. *Sancte Dei pretiose*
   Holy Stephen, first martyr, beloved of God, thou who art supported on all sides by the virtue of charity didst pray to God for thine enemies the people. Pray for us now, thy devoted brethren; so that by thy intervention the Lord may be propitiated and allow us, purged of our sins, to join the company of heaven.

2. *Alleluia: Post partum*
   Alleluia: After childbirth thou didst remain a virgin: O Mother of God, intercede for us, Alleluia.

3. *Perspice Christicola*
   Followers of Christ, observe how condescending is the heavenly husbandman, who for a blemish in the vine spared not his Son but exposed Him to the fate of death. Prisoners half-dead from suffering He restores to life, and crowns them with Him on the throne of heaven.

4. *Miles Christi Gloriose*

   Three Voices: Most holy Edward, renowned soldier of Christ, by thy devout mediation wash away our faults.

   Alto (Tenor) Solo: Hail, warrior, by whose exploits
   the court of heaven is adorned and made joyful:
   who because of a life of praiseworthy merit
   now reignest in the glory of heaven.
   Now the church militant sweetly proclaims
   to Christ, thy praises, that by thy mediation
   it may be cleared of the accusation it laments,
   from which it prays to be free:
   give us good fortune and wash away our wickedness.

I am grateful to Sidney Arthur for his assistance in the translation of some of these passages—*D.S.*

Q

Tenor Solo:　　　　Hail O Edward the warrior, star of saintliness,
　　　　　　　　　　Radiance of virtue, who didst spurn earthly power:
　　　　　　　　　　Thou didst wholeheartedly follow in the footsteps of Christ
　　　　　　　　　　from childhood, by way of poverty and holy charity,
　　　　　　　　　　now in the kingdom of splendour thou art
　　　　　　　　　　redolent with the scent of sweetness:
　　　　　　　　　　we pray thee cleanse our frail souls of sin.

5. *Epiphaniam Domino*
　i Let us duly magnify
　　This renowned Epiphany,
　　To the Child of God today
　　Wise men rightful homage pay.
　　Whom, immeasurably great,
　　Chaldee sages venerate,
　　To whose coming, man to save,
　　All the prophets witness gave:
　　His majestic throne on high—
　　Such his great humility—
　　He refused not to forsake,
　　And a servant's form to take;
　　God from all eternity,
　　Ere the world began to be,
　　He was man of Mary made:

　iii Angel-warned, no word they bring
　　Back to Herod, ruthless king,
　　Fearing much, in rage and hate,
　　He should lose his royal state.
　　Lo! the star before them went,
　　Homeward on their journey bent,
　　Glad they seek their native land.
　　Heeding not the king's command.
　　Maddened with exceeding ire
　　Forth he sends the mandate dire
　　Throughout Bethlehem's coasts to seek
　　And to slay the infants meek.

　ii Whom predicting Balaam said:
　　Out of Jacob, seen from far,
　　There shall come a flaming star,
　　Which with power shall smite the host
　　Of Moab to his utmost coast.
　　Him their costly offering,
　　Gold, myrrh, incense, wise men bring.
　　God, sweet incense; precious gold
　　A king; myrrh doth a man unfold:
　　　　　　　Tenor soloists:
　　Whom predicting Balaam told
　　Of a new star bright and bold,
　　Light creating for the world,
　　　Out of Jacob's line.

　　Him their triple offering
　　As they wish the magi bring,
　　Praising Him, King, God, and Man,
　　　By a wondrous power.

　iv Now the choir their voice unite,
　　Organs swell with mystic rite,
　　Bringing to the King of kings,
　　Praise and costly offerings.
　　O'er all kingdoms, o'er all lands,
　　May he spread his sheltering hands,
　　Ever present to defend
　　Unto worlds that never end. Amen.

6. *Salve sancta parens*
　Hail, Holy Mother, who laboured to bear the King who rules heaven and earth for
　ever and ever. Blessed art thou among women, and blessed is the fruit of thy womb.
　Tenor I:　Hail, Mother of the Redeemer, fountain of mercy,
　　　　　　　Vessel of honour, flower of comeliness,
　　　　　　　Palace of the King of Glory,

Bride of heaven's Creator, Lady of clemency,
Chosen light of the Founder, chamber of seemliness,
Virgin of modesty, gem of chastity,
Make us rest with the citizens of joy,
World without end.

Tenor II: Hail, light of the suffering, consoler of men,
Flower and ornament of virgins, bearer of the Son of God,
King of all kings.
Star in the darkness, shining with a ray of splendour,
Bride to the Son of God, seated next to His throne,
Make those praising thee see the glory of heaven
With the company of saints.

Bass: Hail, rose without thorn, purple flower,
Medicine to the sick, stream from a sweet fountain,
Shrine of the living God, chamber of the great King,
Placing the Son of God in thy womb,
Mindful of thy prayer for ever and ever,
May the Founder of the ends of the earth be merciful unto us.

Glory be to the Father, and to the Son, and to the Holy Ghost; as it was in the beginning, is now, and ever shall be, world without end. Amen.

7. *Alleluia: Per te Dei genitrix*

Tenor I: Now to the beneficent joys of the Mother of God,
In whom rests the entire trust of our hope,
Let us sing alleluya with gladness in mind.

Tenor II: To the revered joys of the kind Mother of God
In whom rests the entire trust of our hope,
Let us sing alleluia with pious devotion.

Bass: Alleluia.

Choir: Alleluia.

Tenor I: Through thee, Mother of God, nourisher of the supreme offspring, forever inviolate, the way to our homeland lies open and the gate of heavenly joy is unlocked, which through the sin of Eve had before been closed to mankind. Generous giver of pardon from Jacob's line, procreated star, the life lost by the fault of Eve is restored to us, giving us divine and honeyed food from heaven. Holy Virgin, thou didst bear in thy chamber for the world an offspring giving heavenly light; thou, a shining star didst receive a sun hiding beneath a cloud.

Tenor II: Through thee, O blessed, ever inviolate, Holy Mother of God, nourisher of a divine offspring, the gate to the heavenly homeland, formerly closed, is unlocked for us. The sentence of death was passed on mankind for the fault of treachery through Eve's sinfulness, until by thy childbirth the blemished stock was given new life. Thou didst receive a divine offspring from heaven, as a star would receive a sun, giving us heavenly light. Thou didst conceive Christ through the voice of the angel, and thou, a virgin, gave birth to Him, bringing honeyed food to a sad world.

Bass: Through thee, Mother of God, our lost life is restored to us; thou didst receive an offspring from heaven, and bore a Saviour for the world.

8.   *Candens lilium columbina*

Tenor I: White lily, dove, fountain of our race,
        Rose growing without a thorn, thou art called Mother.
        Hail, Queen of Virgins, bearing Christ the Lord,
        Sweet is the beginning.
        Thou art the light of lights and saviour of men,
        Sweet is the ending.
        All sinners call upon thee with indulgence
        That we may enjoy the pardon of life-giving rest.
        Beseech thy Son with sincere prayers that the glory of life
        Be granted to all who serve thee by His grace.
        All sinners call upon thee with indulgence
        That we may enjoy the pardon of life-giving rest.

Tenor II: White grows the lily: the virginal womb
        Brings forth into the world a Son, Creator of all things,
        King of ruling kings;
        So that Adam's debt, formerly contracted
        Through the forbidden fruit by the serpent's guile,
        Might be redeemed by the precious blood of the King,
        And that He might rescue Adam from the earth's maw,
        And the patriarchs and prophets born of his seed,
        So that heavenly life might be restored to the ancients in
          magnificent peace.
        Therefore let us sing today a song of gladness about the King of glory,
        That we may enjoy ageless repose in the ranks of heaven.

9.   *Sanctus & Benedictus*

Holy, Holy, Holy, Lord God of Hosts, heaven and earth are full of thy glory. Hosanna in the highest. Blessed is he that cometh in the name of the Lord. Hosanna in the highest.

10. *Agnus Dei*

Lamb of God, that takest away the sins of the world,
   have mercy upon us.
Lamb of God, that takest away the sins of the world,
   have mercy upon us.
Lamb of God, that takest away the sins of the world,
   grant us thy peace.

11. *Beata viscera*
    Blessed is the womb of the Virgin Mary
    Which, heavy with fruit of the everlasting seed,
    Carried with care the drink of sweetness
    In the cup of life for mankind.

12. *Alleluia psallat*
    Alleluia let this congregation sing to the Lord,
    Alleluia clash the cymbals,
    Alleluia sound the harp in joyful company with harmony.
    Alleluia let us sing in jubilation to the Lord.
    Alleluia.

13. *Fulget Caelestis Curia*
    Tenor: The Court of Heaven gleams resplendent
       Where Peter sits as guardian
       Beneath the Prince of Glory.
       Rome delights in such a patron,
       Patron, by God's favour given
       Let the World resound with approbation
       Of the right by Peter taken
       To show that man is not forsaken
       And free us all from mortal sin
       O Peter do thou look on us
       And from us all those things drive out
       For which we merit punishment.
    Tenor: Pre-eminent Apostle Peter
       O Shepherd of the Heavenly Court
       Feed thy sheep by sweetly speaking
       Showing them the way to bliss.
       Warm our hearts with happiness
       Defend us in our wickedness
       Lift the weight of our transgression
       Supplicate, for us, indulgence
       From the highest Prince of Heaven
       Lead us to sublimest joys.
    Tenor: While Rome delights in such a patron,
       Patron, by God's favour given
       The Court of Heaven gleams resplendent
       Where Peter sits as guardian
       Beneath the Prince of Glory.
       Defend and grant us absolution
       Let the world resound with approbation
       Of the right by Peter taken
       To set us free from mortal sin.

14. *Civitas nusquam conditur*

Tenor: A city is never founded and placed on top of a high mountain, nor does one light a shining lamp and hide it under a bushel, but rather is it fixed in a candelabrum aloft, that it might give light to those who walk in darkness. For he who lacks light knows not whither to turn his steps; he knows not whether he is travelling purposefully or whether badly off the track. Thus do the many deeds and teachings of Edward shine openly, not hiding from people who lack light. He offers them the light of true salvation, of wisdom and clemency, and the talents entrusted to him by the Lord he increases an hundredfold, like the good servant; so that glory is accorded him, and he will never be deprived of joy, even unto the end of time.

Bass: The happy citizens of the heavenly kingdom today rejoice in the expectation that Edward will be received into the company of the saints, because this joining together of good men is a sweet and harmonious event, deserving of remembrance in years to come. How sweet too is the helpful dwelling together in the palace on high, before the heavenly King, where today Edward is raised up in joy; and by his prayers may we be led to the company of those who live forever.

15. *Ave Miles Caelestis Curiae*

Alto and Viola: Hail warrior of the heavenly court
Whom the reward of victory adorns
Thou livest with God enjoying repose
After the manner of heaven's inhabitants.

Alto and Viola: Hail King, Protector
Morning light of thy native Saxony
Star of the Anglian peoples
Shining on us in the South.
Now thou rejoicest with the citizens of Heaven
O Martyr Edmund thou art more distinguished than others
Yet thou dost not forsake thy people
Whose devotion to thee thou didst know
Thou dost by prayer make the lame walk again,
Thou healest leprosy, thou dost set slaves free,
Events encourage belief in the legend
The blind see, the dead rise again
Thou dost restrain enemies by fair judgment
Thou sparest slaves with a gracious heart
For the intercession of so strong a king
Let us devoutly bless the Lord
Make us, O Martyr, during our life
Return worthy praises to the Lord.

16. *Kyrie eleison*
Lord have mercy upon us.
Christ have mercy upon us.
Lord have mercy upon us.

17. *Gloria in escelsis Deo*
Glory be to God on high, and in earth peace, good will towards men. We praise
Thee, we bless Thee, we worship Thee, we glorify Thee, we give thanks to Thee
for Thy great glory. O Lord God, heavenly King, God the Father Almighty. O
Lord, the only-begotten Son, Jesu Christ, O Lord God, Lamb of God, Son of the
Father, Thou that takest away the sins of the world, have mercy upon us. Thou
that takest away the sins of the world, receive our prayer. Thou that sittest at the
right hand of God the Father, have mercy upon us. For Thou only art holy, Thou
only art the Lord, Thou only, O Christ, with the Holy Ghost, art most high in the
glory of God the Father. Amen.

18. *Sanctus & Benedictus*
(See No. 9)

19. *Agnus Dei*
(See No. 10)

20. *Conditor alme siderum*

i Creator of the stars of night,
Thy people's everlasting light,
Jesu, Redeemer, save us all,
And hear thy servants when they call.

ii Thou, grieving that the ancient curse
Should doom to death a universe,
Hast found the medicine, full of grace,
To save and heal a ruined race.

iii Thou camest, the Bridegroom of the bride,
As drew the world to evening-tide;
Proceeding from a virgin shrine,
The spotless Victim all divine.

iv At whose dread name, majestic now,
All knees must bend, all hearts must bow;
And things celestial thee shall own,
And things terrestrial, Lord alone.

v O thou whose coming is with dread
To judge and doom the quick and dead,
Preserve us, while we dwell below,
From every insult of the foe.

vi To God the Father, God the Son,
And God the Spirit, Three in One,
Laud, honour, might, and glory be,
From age to age eternally. Amen.

21. *Angelus ad Virginem*
Soprano, Soprano, Alto:

i An Angel to the maiden came
Stealing to her chamber
Her fears he soothed caressingly
And greeting her cried 'Ave!'
Hail O Queen of Virgins pure
Thou, a maiden, wilt conceive
And bear the Lord of Heaven and earth
The Saviour of the world.
Thou of Heaven the gateway art
The remedy for sin.

ii How can it be I shall conceive
Since I have known not any man?
How can I break the vow I made
With such a firm resolve?
Be sure the Holy Spirit's Grace
Will accomplish all these things.
Be not afraid but joyful be
Certain that thy chastity
Undefiled still will be
By the power of God.

22. *Deo Gracias Persolvamus*
                              Refrain
        Alto, Tenor: Let us cheerfully give thanks to God
                              Verse
                Thanks to God, for the most High, born of the virgin's womb
            Let us cheerfully give thanks to God
                Thanks to God, for the king in the crib with gifts adored
            Let us cheerfully give thanks to God
                Thanks to God, his resurrection shone forth on the third day
            Let us cheerfully give thanks to God
                Thanks to God, for the son of Mary let us bless the Lord
            Let us cheerfully give thanks to God

23. *Gloria in excelsis*
    Glory be to God on high, and in earth peace, good will towards men. We praise
    Thee, we bless Thee, we worship Thee, we glorify Thee, we give thanks to Thee
    for Thy great glory. O Lord God, heavenly King, God the Father Almighty. O
    Lord, the only-begotten Son, Jesu Christ:
        Spirit and kind comforter of orphans,
    O Lord God, Lamb of God, Son of the Father:
        First-born of Mary the Virgin Mother,
    Thou that takest away the sins of the world, have mercy upon us.
    Thou that takest away the sins of the world, receive our prayer:
        To the glory of Mary,
    Thou that sittest at the right hand of God the Father, have mercy upon us.
    For Thou only art holy:
        Sanctifying Mary,
    Thou only art the Lord:
        Governing Mary,
    Thou only art most high:
        Crowning Mary,
    O Christ, with the Holy Ghost, in the glory of God the Father. Amen.

24. *Sanctus & Benedictus*
    (See No. 9)

25. *Agnus Dei*
    (See No. 10)

26. *Beata Dei genitrix*
    O Blessed Mary, Mother of God, Virgin for everlasting, temple of the Lord,
    sanctuary of the Holy Ghost, Thou alone and unequalled didst please the Lord
    Jesus Christ. O pray for the people, intervene for the clergy, intercede for the nuns.
                                                                    Alleluia.

27. *Ave regina caelorum*
    Hail, Queen of heaven; hail, Lady of the angels; hail, sacred root from which
    came light into the world. Hail, most glorious, beautiful above all others. Fare
    thee well, O exceeding wondrous Lady, and pray for us to Christ for ever.

28. *Veni sancte spiritus*
Soprano:

i Come, thou holy Paraclete,
And from thy celestial seat,
Send thy light and brilliancy.
Father of the poor, draw near,
Giver of all gifts, be here,
Come, the soul's true radiancy.

ii Come, of comforters the best,
Of the soul the sweetest guest,
Come in toil refreshingly:
Thou in labour rest most sweet,
Thou art shadow from the heat,
Comfort in adversity.

iii O thou Light, most pure and blest,
Shine within the inmost breast,
Of thy faithful company.
Where thou art not, man hath nought,
Every holy deed and thought
Comes from thy divinity.

iv What is soiled, make thou pure;
What is wounded, work its cure;
What is parched, fructify.
What is rigid, gently bend;
What is frozen, warmly tend;
Strengthen what goes erringly.

v Fill thy faithful, who confide
In thy power to guard and guide,
With thy sevenfold mystery.
Here thy grace and virtue send:
Grant salvation to the end,
And in heaven felicity.

Alto:

vi Come, Holy Spirit, and sprinkle the dew of heavenly grace. Save us
divinely who sin as humans, save us from the serpent in whose presence
our bodies are protected by thy mercy. Make our service and our
penitent hearts acceptable unto thee. Consoler of the weary and re-
former of erring ones, medicine of death, forgiver of sins, be a purifier
unto us and lead us to things divine.

Tenor:

vii Come, O Creator Spirit, come,
And make within our hearts thy home;
To us thy grace celestial give,
Who of thy breathing move and live.

viii O Comforter, that name is thine,
Of God most high the gift divine;
The well of life, the fire of love,
Our soul's anointing from above.

ix Thou dost appear in sevenfold dower
The sign of God's almighty power;
The Father's promise, making rich
With saving truth our earthly speech.

x Our senses with thy light inflame,
Our hearts to heavenly love reclaim;
Our bodies' poor infirmity
With strength perpetual fortify.

xi Our mortal foe afar repel,
Grant us henceforth in peace to dwell;
And so to us, with thee for guide,
No ill shall come, no harm betide.

xii May we by thee the Father learn,
And know the Son, and thee discern,
Who art of both; and thus adore
In perfect faith for evermore.

29. *Regina caeli laetare*
O Queen of heaven, rejoice, Alleluia; for thou wert worthy to bear Christ,
Alleluia; He rose again, as he said, Alleluia; pray God for us, Alleluia.

30. *Quam pulchra es*

How beautiful and fair thou art, my beloved, and how desirable. Thy stature is like unto a palm tree, and thy breasts like unto fruit. Thy head is like Mount Carmel, and thy neck like a tower of ivory. Come, my beloved, let us step into the meadows, and see if the blossoms have borne fruit and the pomegranates have flowered. There will I give my breasts to you. Alleluia.

My soul doth magnify the Lord: and my spirit hath rejoiced in God my Saviour.
For he hath regarded the lowliness of his handmaiden: for behold, from hence-
  forth all generations shall call me blessed.
For he that is mighty hath magnified me: and holy is his Name.
And his mercy is on them that fear him: through all generations.
He hath shewed strength with his arm: he hath scattered the proud in the imagi-
  nation of their hearts.
He hath put down the mighty from their seat: and hath exalted the humble and
  meek.
He hath filled the hungry with good things: and the rich he hath sent empty away.
He remembering his mercy hath holpen his servant Israel,
As he promised to our forefathers, Abraham and his seed, for ever.
Glory be to the Father, and to the Son, and to the Holy Ghost,
As it was in the beginning, is now, and ever shall be, world without end. Amen.

31. *Gloria, laus et honor*

Glory and praise and dominion be thine,
King Christ the Redeemer:
Children in sweetness and grace
Raised their hosannas to thee.

Israel's King art thou,
King David's glorious offspring,
Thou that approachest, a King,
Blest in the name of the Lord.

Glory and praise. . . .

Thee in the height extol
Thine angels, thronging around thee,
Man with nature on earth
Joining, in act to adore.

Glory and praise. . . .

Palm leaves bearing on high
Came Hebrew crowds to thy welcome;
We with our prayers and our hymns
Now to thy presence draw near.

Glory and praise. . . .

32. *Salve Virgo Mater*

Alto, Tenor, Bass:

i Hail O Virgin Mother, Holy
The prophecy through thee, O Mary
Has clothed with flesh the Father's word

ii Hail, for Christ her son redeemed us
Christ her son was put to death
And suffered for us greatly

iii Hail O Queen of Heaven's realm
Through whom the panacea is given
To Jews and Gentiles equally

iv Welcome, thou the life restorer
Empress made, of all the guilty
Dwelling in Hell's murky shades

v Do thou cause the word incarnate
To look on us benignantly
Propitiated by thy prayers

vi By thy holy prayer refine us
Keep us from impurity
And from the hatefulness of sin.

33. *Ave Maria Mater Dei*

Counter-Tenor: Hail Mary
   Tenor   Mother of God, Queen of Heaven, Mistress of the World
   Tenor   Empress of Hell
   Bass   Have pity on me
               and on all Christian people
           And suffer us not to be in mortal sin
               but to fulfil thy entire most holy will
           Amen.

34. *Magnificat*

My soul doth magnify the Lord: and my spirit hath rejoiced in God my Saviour.
For he hath regarded the lowliness of his handmaiden: for behold, from henceforth all generations shall call me blessed.
For he that is mighty hath magnified me: and holy is his Name.
And his mercy is on them that fear him: through all generations.
He hath shewed strength with his arm: he hath scattered the proud in the imagination of their hearts.
He hath put down the mighty from their seat: and hath exalted the humble and meek.
He hath filled the hungry with good things: and the rich he hath sent empty away.
He remembering his mercy hath holpen his servant Israel,
As he promised to our forefathers, Abraham and his seed, for ever.
Glory be to the Father, and to the Son, and to the Holy Ghost,
As it was in the beginning, is now, and ever shall be, world without end. Amen.

35. *Gaude Flore Virginali*

Soprano, Alto, Tenor, Tenor, Bass:

 i Rejoice in the virginal flower
    And in her especial honour
    Exceeding the shining
    Pre-eminence of the Angels
    And the adornment of the Saints
    Rewarded with honour.

 iv Rejoice in submission of thy will
     And in the comprehending love
     With God on high thou art united
     So thou mayest follow any vow
     It please a virgin to request
     From Jesus sweetest Jesus.

 ii Rejoice in the beloved wife of God
     For as the clear light of day
     Is given by the brightness of the sun
     So thou truly makest the world
     To shine with the fulness of the
     Light of thy peace.

 v Rejoice O Mother of the wretched
    Because the Father of the Ages
    Will give to those who worship thee
    Fitting punishment on earth
    And a blesséd place above
    In the realm of Heaven celestial.

 iii Rejoice brilliant vessel of virtues
      At whose command hangs
      the whole court of heaven
      Honouring thee in Glory
      Beneficent and fortunate
      Worthy mother of Jesus.

 vi Rejoice O Virgin mother of Christ
     Because, most Holy Virgin,
     Thou alone hast merited
     To be so greatly dignified
     That thy position is the next
     Beneath the Holy Trinity.

 vii   Rejoice O Virgin Mother pure
       Securely so remaining
       These seven stanzas will not end
       Nor decrease but will endure
       And flourish through all time to come   For ever Amen.

36. *Agnus Dei*
     (see No. 10)

37. *Magnificat*
     (see No. 34)

BIBLIOGRAPHY

Abraham, G. (ed.): *The New Oxford History of Music,* Volume III. (Oxford University Press, 1960.)

Apel, W.: *The Notation of Polyphonic Music 900–1600.* (Mediaeval Academy of America: Cambridge, Mass., 1949.)

Bukofzer, M.: *Studies in Medieval and Renaissance Music.* (Dent, 1950.)

Harrison, F.: *Music in Medieval Britain.* (Routledge, 1958.)

Harvey, J. H.: *The Plantagenets* (Batsford, 1948.)

Hughes, Dom A. (ed.): *The New Oxford History of Music,* Volume II. (Oxford University Press, 1954.)

Lang, P. H.: *Music in Western Civilization.* (Dent, 1941.)

Reese, G.: *Music in the Middle Ages.* (Dent, 1940.); *Music in the Renaissance.* (Dent, 1954.)

Robertson, A. and Stevens, D. (ed.): *The Pelican History of Music*; Volume I (1960), Volume II (1963). (Penguin Books.)

Stevens, D.: *Tudor Church Music.* (Faber and Faber, 1961.)

Fayrfax: Magnificat "Regale"
(Oxford, Bodleian Library, Lat. liturg. a.9, fol. 5)

224

DISCOGRAPHY

(a)   Anthologies:—

History of Music in Sound, Vol. II (Early Medieval Music): HMV (HLP 3 and HLP 4)
History of Music in Sound, Vol. III (Ars Nova and Renaissance): HMV (HLP 5, 6 and 7)
Early Music from England, etc.: Telefunken 9432
English Polyphony of the thirteenth and early fourteenth centuries: EA24
English Polyphony of the fourteenth and early fifteenth centuries: EA31

(b)   Composers:—

Dunstable, John, *Sacred and Secular Music*: EA36 (Poulter, Oberlin, Ambrosian Singers; cond. Denis Stevens)
Dunstable, John, *Motets*: APM14069 (Pro Musica Antiqua, Brussels, cond. Safford Cape)
(Pro Musica Antiqua, Brussels, cond. Safford Cape)
Fayrfax, Robert, *Missa Tecum principium; Aeterne laudis lilium*: AMS38 (Ambrosian Singers; cond. Denis Stevens)
Taverner, John, *Missa Gloria tibi Trinitas; In pace in idipsum*: AMS34 (Pro Musica Sacra; cond. Bruno Turner)
Taverner, John, *Kyrie Le Roy; Mass 'The Western Wind'; Dum transisset Sabbatum; Christe Jesu; Mater Christi*:
ZRG5316 (Choir of King's College, Cambridge; cond. David Willcocks)

N.B. The Telefunken and AMS labels are German, the EA is American. They can be ordered through specialist dealers in imported records.

The following items from the present volume have been recorded on HMV (Ambrosian Singers and Players; cond. Denis Stevens):

1. Sancte Dei pretiose	20. Conditor alme siderum
3. Perspice Christicola	23. Gloria in excelsis (Queldryk)
6. Salve sancta parens	24. Sanctus and Benedictus (Excetre)
9. Sanctus and Benedictus	26. Beata Dei Genetrix (Damett)
12. Alleluia psallat	28. Veni Sancte Spiritus (Dunstable)
15. Ave miles caelestis curiae	32. Salve virgo mater (Frye)

33. Ave Maria mater Dei (Cornysh)

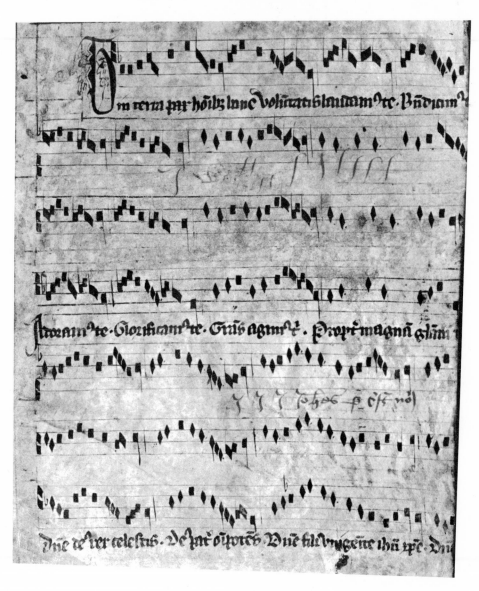

Gloria in excelsis (anon)

(British Museum, Sloane MS. 1270, fol. 138v.)